# INTRODUCTION TO
# CHEMISTRY

## LABORATORY MANUAL

### THIRD EDITION

MICHAEL HAILU

COLUMBUS STATE
Community
College

Learning Solutions

Boston   Burr Ridge, IL   Dubuque, IA   New York   San Francisco   St. Louis
Bangkok   Bogotá   Caracas   Lisbon   London   Madrid
Mexico City   Milan   New Delhi   Seoul   Singapore   Sydney   Taipei   Toronto

# INTRODUCTION TO CHEMISTRY
# LABORATORY MANUAL, THIRD EDITION

6 7 8 9 0  KNG KNG 15 14

ISBN-13: 978-0-07-804564-6
ISBN-10: 0-07-804564-9

Learning Solutions Manager: Brad Ritter
Production Editor: Vanessa Arnold
Cover Photo: Side by side test tubes showing the reaction between zinc and acids. Copyright © The McGraw-Hill Companies, Inc./Stephen Frisch, photographer
Cover Design: Fairfax Hutter
Printer/Binder: King Printing

# ACKNOWLEDGMENTS

I would like to thank Dr. Lud Sprandel at Columbus State Community College for his valuable contributions and extensive editions on the chemistry 100 laboratory manual. Basically, the lecture supplement-course objectives, review sheets and worksheets are contributed by my colleague Dr. Lud Sprandel.

In addition, I express my gratitude to Dr. Marc Lord of Columbus State Community College for his review the manual. I also extend my thanks to Dr. Larry Mayer the chairman of the Biological and Physical Sciences Department of Columbus State Community College for his valuable advice and leadership in completing this project.

# TABLE OF CONTENTS

## LABORATORY MANUAL - EXPERIMENTS

## LECTURE SUPPLEMENT - COURSE OBJECTIVES

# LABORATORY MANUAL

---

# EXPERIMENTS

# POLICIES AND PROCEDURES
# LABORATORY DRESS CODE

1.  Safety goggles meeting ANSI Z87.1 are required for all students.
2.  The use of contact lenses is discouraged.
3.  Opened toed/open heeled sandals or canvas shoes are prohibited.
4.  No loose fitting garments, no bare mid-rift, or exposed legs or arms.
5.  No shorts at any time.
6.  Lab coats are provided if wanted, but are not mandatory.
7.  Appropriate chemical resistance gloves are provided if wanted, but are not considered mandatory.
8.  Long hair must be tied back and out of the way of open flame.

# RULES

1.  No horse playing at any time.
2.  No food or beverage allowed at anytime.
3.  No chewing of gum is allowed.
4.  No unauthorized experiments in labs.

NOTE: Persons without appropriate attire are required to leave the laboratory.

# INTRODUCTION TO THE LABORATORY

## Objective

Your objective in this laboratory is to learn important safety rules and basic techniques that are necessary for working safely and efficiently in a chemistry lab. You will inventory the equipment in your assigned locker, view a safety video, and practice some lab procedures.

## Introduction

An academic chemistry laboratory is the place where students perform experiments for educational purposes. These experiments illustrate and enhance theoretical and descriptive material being studied in chemistry lecture. It is essential that students perform their experiments in a safe manner, and it is important that they work efficiently in the laboratory.

To ensure safety in the laboratory, students must follow certain safety rules and procedures. These will be reviewed in the video *Starting with Safety*. While there are many aspects to lab safety, safety equipment and waste disposal are of prime importance. Students must wear their own splash-resistant safety goggles when working in the lab. Students must know the locations of the shower, eyewash, fire extinguisher, and fire blanket and how to operate them. Waste and excess chemicals must be disposed of in proper waste containers, and never in the sink or trash can. As part of their safety training, students will be required to complete a safety quiz and sign a safety agreement.

To work efficiently in the lab, students must be familiar with the identity and use of various pieces of equipment and glassware found in the laboratory. To accomplish this, students will inventory the equipment in their assigned locker and practice some lab procedures such as using a balance, reading a graduated cylinder, and lighting a Bunsen burner.

In order to have a safe, productive, and enjoyable lab experience, students should read the experiments ahead of time, work at a comfortable pace, and use common sense at all times in the laboratory. Finally, students must remember to apply what they learn in this lab to all of the experiments that they perform. Safety and the use of proper lab techniques are ongoing concerns in this course.

# Procedure

A. Equipment inventory

1. An equipment locker will be assigned to you. Remove the contents of the locker, placing all the items on the lab bench.

2. Using the **CHEMISTRY LOCKER INVENTORY** sheet and the **LABORATORY EQUIPMENT** sheet, make an inventory of your equipment. Note the correct name of each piece of equipment, and return each item to your locker as you check it off the list.

3. Replace any broken or missing items with equipment from the lab supply cabinet. Return extra items and any equipment not on the inventory list to the place indicated by your instructor.

4. Note that students in other courses will also use your locker. Therefore, it is important that you clean your glassware before leaving the lab.

B. Laboratory safety

1. Your instructor will show a video entitled *Starting with Safety*, which reviews the safety rules that are important for your laboratory.

2. While watching the video, complete the **Safety Quiz**. Note that the quiz is correlated to the various sections of the video. When requested, submit the quiz to your instructor.

3. Your instructor will then discuss lab safety and show you the location of the shower, eyewash, fire extinguisher, and fire blanket.

4. Using the **CHEMISTRY LABORATORY SAFETY RULES/AGREEMENT** sheet, carefully read the summarized **Safety Rules** that are pertinent to the laboratory and complete and sign both copies of the **Safety Agreement**. When requested, submit one of the copies to your instructor.

C. Laboratory techniques

   1. Your instructor will demonstrate a number of lab
      procedures that you will be required to perform as this
      course progresses.

      a. Using a balance; determining mass by difference
      b. Using a graduated cylinder; reading the meniscus
      c. Lighting and adjusting a Bunsen burner
      d. Heating a test tube with a Bunsen burner
      e. Heating a crucible or beaker; using the ring stand and
         iron ring
      f. Disposing of waste and excess chemicals

   2. Practice using the balance, graduated cylinder, and Bunsen
      burner.

# CHEMISTRY LOCKER INVENTORY

1 - apron or lab coat

1 - beaker, 100-mL

1 - beaker, 250-mL

1 - beaker, 400-mL

1 - beaker, 600-mL

1 - Bunsen burner with tubing

1 - clamp

1 - clay triangle

1 - crucible with cover

1 - Erlenmeyer flask, 50-mL

1 - Erlenmeyer flask, 125-mL

1 - Erlenmeyer flask, 250-mL

1 - funnel

1 - graduated cylinder, 10-mL

1 - graduated cylinder, 50-mL

1 - graduated cylinder, 100-mL

1 - iron ring

2 - medicine droppers

1 - mortar and pestle

4 - rubber stoppers, size 0

1 - scoop

1 - stirring rod

1 - test tube holder

1 - test tube rack

9 - test tubes, 16x150-mm

3 - test tubes, 25x200-mm

1 - tongs

1 - towel

1 - watch glass

1 - water bottle

1 - wax pencil

1 - wire screen

# LABORATORY EQUIPMENT

lab coat

beaker

Bunsen burner

Erlenmeyer flask

funnel

graduated cylinder

medicine dropper

stirring rod

test tube and holder

tongs

watch glass

clamp and iron ring on ring stand

# INTRODUCTION TO
# THE LABORATORY

Name _____

Date _____

## Safety Quiz

1. What does the video tell you about the size of the containers that you should use when pouring chemicals?


2. When should you mix chemicals?


3. What does the video tell you about touching, tasting, and smelling chemicals?


4. What should you do with excess chemicals you have not used?


5. What should you do when you have finished your experiment?


6. State one rule about Bunsen burner use.

   *Smell gas, tune it off*

7. What should you do if an alcohol thermometer breaks?

   *A glass or anything must be "cleanned up, and should be down by the teacher*

8. State one rule about appropriate dress for the laboratory.

   *Protect your hand* *Remove ring and watches never use bare hands to work with chemicals*

9. State one rule about appropriate lab behavior.

   *no fooleing around. dont eat in the lab, keep makeup in your bag*

10. State one rule about emergency equipment.

    *Notify you techer immently you have a Cut*

# CHEMISTRY LABORATORY SAFETY RULES/AGREEMENT

The student is required to read the safety rules carefully and to give this agreement, signed and dated, to the instructor.

## Safety Rules

1. Absolutely no unauthorized experiments should be attempted.
2. Safety goggles must be worn at all times in the laboratory.
3. Know the location of safety equipment and how to use it.
4. Wear sensible clothing. Aprons must be worn at all times.
5. While in the laboratory, never put anything in your mouth.
6. Use the fume hood when necessary.
7. Keep the laboratory clean.
8. Use only equipment that is in good condition.
9. Never work alone.
10. Dispose of waste and excess materials in the proper manner.
11. Avoid touching hot objects.
12. Use extreme caution when inserting glass into stoppers.
13. Handle chemicals with caution.
    a. Read the labels carefully.
    b. Use only what is needed.
    c. Leave chemicals in their proper place.
    d. All spills must be cleaned up immediately.
    e. Label all chemicals.
14. Report immediately all accidents that cause injury, no matter how minor, to the laboratory instructor.
15. No visitors are allowed in the laboratory.
16. Food and beverages are not permitted in the laboratory.
17. When in the laboratory, think and use common sense and good judgment about what you are doing at all times.

## Safety Agreement

As a condition to my enrollment in this chemistry course, I have read carefully all the safety rules that are summarized above and agree to observe them through the duration of the course. I assume the risk and the responsibility for any injuries that are caused by or result from my failure to observe these safety rules.

Signature _____     Course _____

Print name _____     Section _____

Date _____     (Instructor's copy)

# CHEMISTRY LABORATORY SAFETY RULES/AGREEMENT

The student is required to read the safety rules carefully and to give this agreement, signed and dated, to the instructor.

## Safety Rules

1. Absolutely no unauthorized experiments should be attempted.
2. Safety goggles must be worn at all times in the laboratory.
3. Know the location of safety equipment and how to use it.
4. Wear sensible clothing. Aprons must be worn at all times.
5. While in the laboratory, never put anything in your mouth.
6. Use the fume hood when necessary.
7. Keep the laboratory clean.
8. Use only equipment that is in good condition.
9. Never work alone.
10. Dispose of waste and excess materials in the proper manner.
11. Avoid touching hot objects.
12. Use extreme caution when inserting glass into stoppers.
13. Handle chemicals with caution.
    a. Read the labels carefully.
    b. Use only what is needed.
    c. Leave chemicals in their proper place.
    d. All spills must be cleaned up immediately.
    e. Label all chemicals.
14. Report immediately all accidents that cause injury, no matter how minor, to the laboratory instructor.
15. No visitors are allowed in the laboratory.
16. Food and beverages are not permitted in the laboratory.
17. When in the laboratory, think and use common sense and good judgment about what you are doing at all times.

## Safety Agreement

As a condition to my enrollment in this chemistry course, I have read carefully all the safety rules that are summarized above and agree to observe them through the duration of the course. I assume the risk and the responsibility for any injuries that are caused by or result from my failure to observe these safety rules.

Signature _____      Course _____

Print name _____      Section _____

Date _____      (Student's copy)

# METRIC MEASUREMENTS

## Objective

The objective of this experiment is to measure lengths, masses, and volumes using metric units. In the laboratory, you will become proficient with the use of the meter stick, the electronic balance, and the graduated cylinder.

## Introduction

Measurement is the comparison of a physical quantity to be measured with a unit of measurement. A measurement determines the quantity, dimensions, or extent of something in comparison to a specific unit. A unit is a definite quantity adopted as a reference standard. The result of a measurement consists of two parts - a numerical value followed by a specific unit.

The metric system is a system of measurement that was established in France in the 1790s. It consists of a set of base units that correspond to various physical quantities to be measured and a group of prefixes that are used with each base unit to form a series of units having different sizes. Each prefix corresponds to a power of 10. Therefore, each metric unit is related in size to other units of the same type by a power of 10, making the metric system a decimal system of measurement. Use of the metric system gradually spread from France to many other countries and also to the scientific community. The modern version of the metric system is called the International System of Units, or SI. It is the official system of measurement used by most countries in the world and the system of choice of scientists.

The base metric units that will be studied in this lab are the meter (m), the gram (g), and the liter (L), which are used for measuring length, mass, and volume, respectively. The metric prefixes centi- (c), signifying 0.01 or $10^{-2}$, and milli- (m), signifying 0.001 or $10^{-3}$, will be used with these base units to form units such as the centimeter (cm) and the milliliter (mL). To establish a working knowledge of these metric units, you will perform a number of basis laboratory measurements using the meter stick, the electronic balance, and the graduated cylinder.

Every measurement has a degree of uncertainty associated with it that the person making the measurement should strive to reduce to an acceptable level. An experiment is often repeated several times to obtain a replicate set of measurements for comparison. The reproducibility of results obtained by the same experimental method is termed precision. Using a set of individual measurements, an average of the measurements, called the mean, is calculated. The mean is obtained by adding the individual measurements and dividing the result by the number of measurements. For a series of 3 measurements $x_1$, $x_2$, and $x_3$, the mean, $x_{av}$, is given by the following expression.

$$x_{av} = (x_1 + x_2 + x_3)/3$$

The difference between any individual measurement and the mean is used to express the precision of the measurement. The deviation of a measurement $x_i$ from the mean is the absolute value of the difference between $x_i$ and the mean.

$$\text{deviation for } x_i = |x_i - x_{av}|$$

The relative deviation is obtained by multiplying the quotient of the deviation for a measured quantity and the mean by 100%.

$$\text{relative deviation for } x_i = (|x_i - x_{av}|/x_{av}) \times 100\%$$

The relative deviation is one method of expressing the precision of a measured quantity.

The closeness of a single measurement to the true value, $x_{true}$, is called accuracy. The difference between a measurement $x_i$ and $x_{true}$ is the error of the measurement.

$$\text{error in } x_i = x_i - x_{true}$$

Note that accuracy, which compares a measured quantity to the true value, is not the same as precision, which compares one measured quantity with the others. The true value is seldom known; the reason why we do experiments is to determine a value for a quantity. Thus, it is difficult to arrive at an estimate of the error of a measurement. The relative error is obtained by multiplying the quotient of the error in a measured quantity and the true value by 100%.

$$\text{relative error in } x_i = ((x_i - x_{true})/x_{true}) \times 100\%$$

The relative error is one method of expressing the accuracy of a measured quantity.

Errors in measured quantities fall into two broad categories – determinate errors and indeterminate errors. Determinate errors are systematic errors whose sources are assignable, such as an instrumental error or an error in the experimental method. Determinate errors affect the accuracy of the measurement. A determinate error will usually affect a given physical measurement in one particular direction.

Indeterminate errors are random errors, which means that they cannot be easily identified. These types of errors usually do not affect a given measurement in the same direction all the time. One common source of indeterminate error is the variation in the experimental technique of the investigator. Given a sufficient number of measurements of the same quantity, this type of error tends to average out, and the average value may approach the true value. The magnitude of this type of error is reflected in the precision of the measurement.

## Materials

table salt (sodium chloride, NaCl) (6 g per group)

meter sticks (1 per group)
unknown samples for mass determination (1 per group)

---

### Safety Precautions

Use normal laboratory safety precautions. Since the table salt is used only for observational purposes, it does not need to be disposed of in a waste container. Return it to the original sample container.

---

## Procedure

It is recommended that students work in groups of 2 or 3 for this experiment.

A. Measuring length

1. **Wear chemical splash-proof goggles at all time while in the laboratory. Your goggles must be approved by your instructor as complying with state eye-protection laws.**

2. Observe the markings on a meter stick. The meter stick is divided into 100 numbered increments. What is the length of one of these numbered increments, which is 1/100 or

0.01 of a meter? If you observe closely, you will notice that each of the 100 numbered increments is divided into 10 un-numbered increments. Therefore, there are 1000 of these un-numbered increments on the meter stick. What is the length of one of these un-numbered increments, which is 1/1000 or 0.001 of a meter?

3. Use the meter stick to answer the following questions.

   a. Find the mark on the meter stick that represents 65 centimeters. How many millimeters are there in 65 centimeters? How many meters?

   b. Find the mark on the meter stick that represents 0.95 meter. How many centimeters are there in 0.95 meters? How many millimeters?

   c. How many meters are there in 170 centimeters? How many millimeters?

   Measure the length, the width, and the height of your laboratory table in centimeters. What is the area of the top in square centimeters? What is the volume of the table in cubic centimeters?

B. Measuring

   1. Obtain an object of unknown mass from the dispensing table and determine its mass to the nearest 0.01 gram. Record the mass and code number of the unknown. Return the unknown to the dispensing table.

   2. Measure out a sample of water using the following steps.

      a. Determine the mass of a 250-mL beaker to the nearest 0.01 gram. This mass is called the tare.

      b. Carefully measure 25.0 milliliters of water in a graduated cylinder. Transfer the water to the 250-mL beaker.

      c. Determine the gross mass of the beaker and the water. Calculate the net mass of the water.

   3. Measure out 5.23 grams of table salt on a piece of weighing paper. Record the gross, tare, and net masses. Retain the measured sample for inspection by your

instructor. The sample may be returned to the original container after inspection.

C. Measuring volume

1. Measure out 6 milliliters of water in both the 10-mL and the 100-mL graduated cylinders. Remember that volumes are measured at the bottom of the meniscus. Record each volume to the proper number of significant figures. Note which cylinder gives the more precise measurement.

2. Measure out 60 milliliters of water in a 250-mL beaker. Pour the water into a 100-mL graduated cylinder and read the volume to the proper number of significant figures. Note which measuring device – the beaker or the graduated cylinder – gives the more accurate measurement.

3. **Once the experiment is completed, clean off all equipment and glassware that you used during this experiment and return them to their proper locations. You must clean off your work area and wash your hands thoroughly with detergent and water before you leave the laboratory.**

2. Obtain a cylindrical metal sample from your instructor. Record the chemical identity and give a brief description (shape, color, etc.) of the sample.

3. Determine the mass of the sample to the nearest 0.01 g. It may be placed directly on the balance pan.

4. Using a metric ruler, carefully measure to the nearest 0.01 cm the height and the diameter of the metal cylinder. Calculate the radius of the cylinder by dividing the diameter by 2.

5. Calculate the volume of the metal cylinder in $cm^3$.

6. Calculate the density of the metal sample in $g/cm^3$.

7. Return the metal cylinder to your instructor.

B. Density of a solid sample with an irregular shape (rubber stopper)

1. Obtain a rubber stopper from your instructor. Give a brief description (shape, color, etc.) of the sample.

2. Determine the mass of the sample to the nearest 0.01 g. It may be placed directly on the balance pan.

3. Fill a 100-mL graduated cylinder approximately halfway with water. Record the volume of the water to the nearest 0.1 mL.

4. Carefully slide the stopper into the graduated cylinder. Try to avoid splashing the water. Make sure that the stopper is completely submerged in the water and that no bubbles adhere to it. Record the volume for the water and the stopper to the nearest 0.1 mL.

5. Determine the volume of the stopper in mL by calculating the volume of water that it displaces.

6. Calculate the density of the rubber stopper in g/mL.

7. Return the stopper to your instructor.

C. Density of a liquid sample

1. Determine the mass of a dry 50-mL graduated cylinder to the nearest 0.01 g.

2. Obtain 25 to 30 mL of the unknown liquid sample in the graduated cylinder. Measure the mass of the cylinder and liquid sample to the nearest 0.01 g.

3. Calculate the mass of the liquid sample.

4. Measure the liquid volume to the nearest 0.1 mL.

5. Calculate the density of the liquid sample in g/mL.

6. Dispose of the liquid sample in the proper waste container.

7. **Once the experiment is completed, clean off all equipment and glassware that you used during this experiment and return them to their proper locations. You must clean off your work area and wash your hands thoroughly with detergent and water before you leave the laboratory.**

# DENSITY

## Prelaboratory Assignment

1. Density is a physical property of matter.

   A. Define physical property.


   B. List three other physical properties of matter.


2. The density of liquid mercury is 13.6 g/mL at 25 °C.

   A. What is the density in $g/cm^3$?


   B. Convert the density to English units of lb/qt.




3. At 25 °C, the dimensions of a rectangular block of gold are 4.42 cm by 3.07 cm by 2.63 cm. The mass of the gold is 689 g.

   A. Calculate the density of gold at 25 °C.




   B. What is the density of a 450 g block of gold at 25 °C?


   C. How will the density change if the temperature is increased to 125 °C? Explain.

# DENSITY

Name _____

Date _____

## Laboratory Report

## Results

A. Density of a solid sample with a regular shape
   (metal cylinder)

Chemical identity of sample      _____

Description of sample:

Mass of sample      _____

Height of cylinder      _____

Diameter of cylinder      _____

Radius of cylinder      _____

Volume of cylinder      _____

Density of sample      _____

Calculations of sample volume and density:

B. Density of a solid sample with an irregular shape
   (rubber stopper)

   Description of sample:



   Mass of sample                      _____

   Volume of water                     _____

   Volume for water and stopper        _____

   Volume of stopper                   _____

   Density of sample                   _____

   Calculations of sample volume and density:




C. Density of a liquid sample

   Mass of graduated cylinder          _____

   Mass of cylinder and sample         _____

   Mass of sample                      _____

   Volume of sample                    _____

   Density of sample                   _____

   Calculations of sample mass and density:

## Questions

1. A. What is the chemical identity of the metal
   cylinder that you used in part A?                        _____

   B. What value did you obtain for the density
   of the metal cylinder?                                   _____

   C. Use the *CRC Handbook of Chemistry and Physics*
   to obtain a literature value for the density
   of this metal.                                           _____

   D. Cite this reference by giving the title, edition, editor,
   section number, and page number.


   E. Using the literature value as the true density, comment on
   the accuracy of your measured density for this metal.


2. A. What value did you obtain for the density
   of the liquid sample in part C?                          _____

   B. This liquid is actually a colorless substance. The color
   you observed was due to a dye that was added to disguise
   the sample. Based on your measured density, what substance
   could this liquid be? Explain.


3. A. What value did you obtain for the density
   of the rubber stopper in part B?                         _____

# PHYSICAL AND CHEMICAL CHANGES

## Objective

The objective of this experiment is to learn how matter can be changed physically and chemically. You will make observations that allow you to distinguish between physical and chemical changes.

## Introduction

A sample of matter can be classified according to the physical and chemical properties it exhibits. Changes in which the physical properties of a substance are altered are called physical changes, while changes in which chemical properties are altered are called chemical changes.

A physical change is one that alters a physical property of a substance without changing its chemical identity. Breaking a piece of glass into small pieces is an example of a physical change. The broken glass still has the same chemical composition and the same chemical properties as the original piece of glass, but the external form of the glass has changed. If liquid water is placed in a freezer, it will change to a solid in a process called freezing. This is another example of a physical change because only the state of the substance has changed. It is still water after it has solidified. Melting, which is the reverse of freezing, and evaporation, which involves a change from the liquid to the vapor state, are additional examples of physical changes.

As another example, consider what happens when table salt (sodium chloride, NaCl) is added to water and dissolved. After the salt has dissolved in the water, you no longer see the white, crystalline solid. However, a change in chemical composition has not occurred. The mixture still contains the water molecules, the sodium ions, and the chloride ions that were present in the original substances. The water and the salt are not converted to other types of substances when they are mixed together. This dissolving process is a physical change.

A characteristic of many physical changes is the fact that they can easily be reversed by changing the direction of heat flow. For example, liquid water can be converted to the solid state, or ice, by removing heat energy. This physical change, called freezing, can be reversed simply by adding heat energy to the ice. The original liquid water is obtained through melting of the ice. A useful characteristic of physical changes is that they can by employed to separate the components of a mixture. Consider a solution containing salt dissolved in water. This solution is a mixture. If the water is allowed to evaporate, the salt will remain behind as a solid. The water vapor can then be condensed back to liquid water. The components of the mixture can be separated and obtained in their original form by using the physical changes of evaporation and condensation.

Chemical changes are changes in which substances are transformed into new substances. For example, sodium, which is a soft, shiny metal, undergoes a chemical change when it is combined with water. The sodium and water react to produce sodium hydroxide and hydrogen gas. The heat produced in this reaction is often sufficient to cause the hydrogen to ignite and burn. This reactivity of sodium with water is a chemical property of the sodium. The change is a chemical change because the original substances, sodium and water, are transformed into new substances, sodium hydroxide and hydrogen.

As another example, consider what happens when sodium and chlorine, which is a green-yellow gas, are combined. When these substances come in contact, a rather incredible thing happens. Large amounts of heat and light energy are produced. When the reaction subsides, the sodium and chlorine are gone. They are replaced by an entirely new substance - the compound sodium chloride. The new compound has chemical properties that are entirely different from those of the substances from which it was made. For example, the sodium chloride does not react with water as sodium does. It is ordinary table salt. The process that occurs when sodium and chlorine are mixed is a chemical change.

In the laboratory, there are certain observations that can be made to determine whether a chemical change has occurred. Energy in the form of heat may be absorbed or released during a chemical change. This can produce a temperature change that might be observed by the sense of touch. Energy in the form of light is released in some chemical changes. This can be observed visually. The products of chemical changes are frequently gases or insoluble precipitates. Visual observation of the formation of bubbles or a solid in a reaction mixture might indicate that a chemical change is occurring. Finally, many chemicals have characteristic colors. Visually observed color changes may indicate chemical changes.

# Materials

sand (0.5 g per group)
sodium chloride (NaCl) (0.5 g per group)
0.3 M silver nitrate (AgNO$_3$) (5 drops per group)

toothpicks (3 per group)
filter paper (2 pieces per group)

## Safety Precautions

**Do not touch hot glass. Use gentle boiling for evaporating a liquid. Avoid skin contact with the silver nitrate solution.**

# Procedure

It is recommended that students work in groups of 2 or 3 for this experiment.

A. Changes involving wood

1. **Wear chemical splash-proof goggles at all time while in the laboratory. Your goggles must be approved by your instructor as complying with state eye-protection laws.**

2. Break three toothpicks into small pieces. Put the pieces into a 25x200-mm test tube.

3. Heat the test tube strongly with a Bunsen burner for several minutes. Record your observations.

B. Changes involving sand and sodium chloride

1. Measure out 0.50 g samples of sand and sodium chloride on different pieces of weighing paper.

2. Mix the two samples together in a 250-mL beaker. Add 50 mL of water and stir. Observe what happens to the sand and to the sodium chloride.

3. Set up a gravity filtration assembly as follows:

   a. Support a funnel on a ring stand using your iron ring and clay triangle.

b. Fold a piece of filter paper in half, and then in quarters, producing a cone.

c. Set the filter paper cone in the funnel with the tip of the cone fitted into the stem of the funnel.

d. Holding the filter paper in place, wet it using distilled water from your water bottle. Pour out the excess water.

4. Filter the contents of the beaker from step 2 into a graduated cylinder. Record the volume of the filtrate collected (liquid that passed through the filter paper).

5. Equip a ring stand with an iron ring and wire screen for heating a beaker with your Bunsen burner.

6. Determine the mass of a clean, dry 250-mL beaker.

7. Add one half of your filtrate from step 4 to this beaker and record the volume of filtrate added. Save the other half portion of the filtrate for step 10.

8. Place the beaker on the ring stand and gently boil the filtrate until all the water evaporates and the remaining substance is completely dry. Then allow the beaker to cool.

9. Determine the mass of the beaker and the substance it contains. Calculate the mass and record the appearance of the substance remaining in the beaker.

10. Record the volume of the remaining portion of the filtrate from step 7 and pour it into a 100-mL beaker. Add 5 drops of 0.3 M silver nitrate solution to the beaker and stir. Record your observation.

11. Set up a filtration assembly as described in step 3 and filter the mixture from step 10.

12. When all the liquid has drained through the filter paper, remove the filter paper from the funnel and spread it out on a watch glass. Record the appearance of the substance on the filter paper being sure to note the color.

13. Place the watch glass and filter paper in a location on your lab bench where there is good exposure to the laboratory lights. Allow the material on the filter paper to be exposed to the light for about 15 minutes. Record

the appearance of the substance after light exposure being sure to note the color.

14. **Once the experiment is completed, clean off all equipment and glassware that you used during this experiment and return them to their proper locations. You must clean off your work area and wash your hands thoroughly with detergent and water before you leave the laboratory.**

# PHYSICAL AND CHEMICAL CHANGES

Name _____

Date _____

## Prelaboratory Assignment

1. Classify the following processes as physical changes or chemical changes.

   A. Conversion of a compound into an element and another compound. _____

   B. Conversion of two compounds into a solution. _____

   C. Conversion of two elements into a compound. _____

2. When sugar is added to water, it dissolves. Does the sugar undergo a physical change or a chemical change? Explain.

3. When ethanol is burned, it is converted into carbon dioxide and water. Does the ethanol undergo a physical change or a chemical change? Explain.

# Chemical Bonding

## Objective

This experiment is designed to help students u⃨ ⃨rstand the concept of the chemical bonding. Students will deter⃨ ⃨e molecular shapes of simple molecules, and use molecu⃨ ⃨ shapes or geometries and electronegativity data to determine⃨ ⃨hether molecules are polar or nonpolar.

## Introduction

The molecular geometry of a molecule is the shape ⃨ ⃨the three-dimensional manner in which the atoms project int⃨ ⃨ace. The shape of a molecule is important because it effects polarity of a molecule. The polarity of a molecule effect physical properties such as solubility, melting point, an boiling point.

In order to predict the molecular geometry or shape o⃨ molecule, one must consider the number of bonds and the num⃨ of lone-pair electrons around the central atom. The arrange⃨ ⃨ of bonds and lone-pair electrons, and whether the bonds are polar or nonpolar, will determine whether the molecule is po⃨ or nonpolar. Whether a bond is polar or nonpolar is determine by the electronegativity difference between the atoms making ⃨ the bond. The electronegativity values for the main group elements are shown in the figure below.

Electronegativities of the Elements

| 1A | | | | | | | | | | | | 3A | 4A | 5A | 6A | 7A |
|----|----|----|----|----|----|----|----|----|----|----|----|----|----|----|----|----|
| 2.1 H | 2A | | | | | | | | | | | | | | | |
| 1.0 Li | 1.5 Be | | | | | | | | | | | 2.0 B | 2.5 C | 3.0 N | 3.5 O | 4.0 F |
| 0.9 Na | 1.2 Mg | | | | | | | | | | | 1.5 Al | 1.8 Si | 2.1 P | 2.5 S | 3.0 Cl |
| 0.8 K | 1.0 Ca | 1.3 Sc | 1.5 Ti | 1.6 V | 1.6 Cr | 1.5 Mn | 1.8 Fe | 1.8 Co | 1.8 Ni | 1.9 Cu | 1.6 Zn | 1.6 Ga | 1.8 Ge | 2.0 As | 2.4 Se | 2.8 Br |
| 0.8 Rb | 1.0 Sr | 1.2 Y | 1.4 Zr | 1.6 Nb | 1.8 Mo | 1.9 Tc | 2.2 Ru | 2.2 Rh | 2.2 Pd | 1.9 Ag | 1.7 Cd | 1.7 In | 1.8 Sn | 1.9 Sb | 2.1 Te | 2.5 I |
| 0.7 Cs | 0.9 Ba | 1.1–1.2 La–Lu | 1.3 Hf | 1.5 Ta | 1.7 W | 1.9 Re | 2.2 Os | 2.2 Ir | 2.2 Pt | 2.4 Au | 1.9 Hg | 1.8 Tl | 1.8 Pb | 1.9 Bi | 2.0 Po | 2.2 At |
| 0.7 Fr | 0.9 Ra | 1.1–1.7 Ac–Lr | | | | | | | | | | | | | | |

Decreasing electronegativity

Increasing electronegativity

Notice that in general, electronegativity increases from left to right and decreases from top to bottom in the table.

The electrons in a bond are shared equally between the atoms when atoms with the same electronegativity value bond with each other. In such a situation, the bond that forms is a nonpolar covalent bond. When the electronegativity difference between two atoms is larger the bond that forms is a polar covalent bond, and if the difference is very large the resulting bond is likely to be ionic. In general, an electronegativity difference between zero and two results in a polar covalent bond. An ionic bond results when the difference is larger than two.

One can predict the polarity of bonds using electronegativity data. However, it is also important to be able to predict the polarity of molecules. The terms polar and nonpolar, when used to describe molecules, refers to the distribution of charge in a molecule. In a polar molecule the charge is unequally distributed. The molecule has one partial positive end and one partial negative end. In a nonpolar molecule the charge is equally distributed and the molecule does not have positive and negative ends. For example, in a fluorine molecule both fluorine atoms have the same electronegativity. As a result both atoms share the two electrons in the covalent bond equally. This results in an equal distribution of charge. As such, fluorine molecules are nonpolar.

$$F \text{ --- } F$$

Carbon dioxide molecules have a linear geometry with the carbon atom in the center. The two oxygen atoms have a higher electronegativity than the carbon atom but have the same electronegativity when compared to each other. The electrons in the two bonds will not be shared equally; they will reside closer to the oxygen atoms because of the higher electronegativity of oxygen. Since the molecule is linear, the overall distribution of charge is symmetrical and the molecule is nonpolar even though the bonds that make up the molecule are polar. The molecule does not have one positive end and one negative end. The partial positive and partial negative charges cancel each other out.

Water molecules, on the other hand, are non-linear or bent. The two hydrogen atoms have a lower electronegativity than oxygen but have the same electronegativity when compared to each other. As such, the electrons in the two bonds will reside closer to the oxygen. Since the water molecule is bent the charge distribution is not symmetrical. The molecule has a partial negative end (on top of the molecule as drawn above) and a partial positive end (on the bottom of the molecule). This unsymmetrical distribution of charge results in a polar molecule. Therefore, in order to determine the polarity of the molecule one must know the correct molecular geometry.

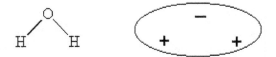

In this experiment, you will build molecules containing covalent bonds using a molecular model kit. A single bond is a covalent bond in which a single pair of electrons is shared between two atoms. A double bond is a covalent bond in which two pairs of electrons are shared between two atoms, and a triple bond is a covalent bond in which three pairs of electrons are shared between two atoms. The number and type of bonds that an atom forms depends on the number of electrons it needs to satisfy the octet rule. For example, a carbon atom has four valence electrons and therefore needs to share four more with other atoms to fulfill the octet rule. This can be accomplished by forming four single bonds, two double bonds, one double and two single, or one triple and one single. In each case, the carbon atom has eight electrons in its outer shell after bonding. In the diagram below, the "A" refers to another atom and the "x"s and dots refer to electrons.

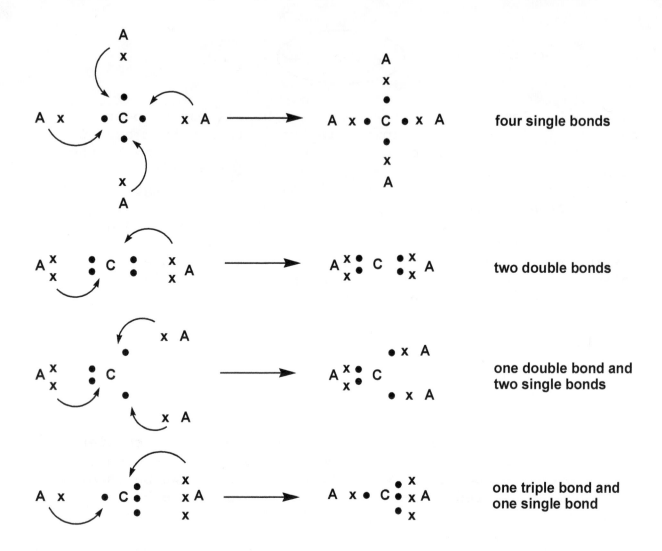

four single bonds

two double bonds

one double bond and
two single bonds

one triple bond and
one single bond

Notice that in each case, the bonds (bonding electrons) are symmetrically spaced around the carbon atom so that all bonds are as far from each other as possible. Similar analyses can be performed with other atoms. For example, nitrogen has five valence electrons and therefore needs three more electrons to fulfill the octet rule. This can be accomplished by forming three single bonds, one double and one single, or one triple.

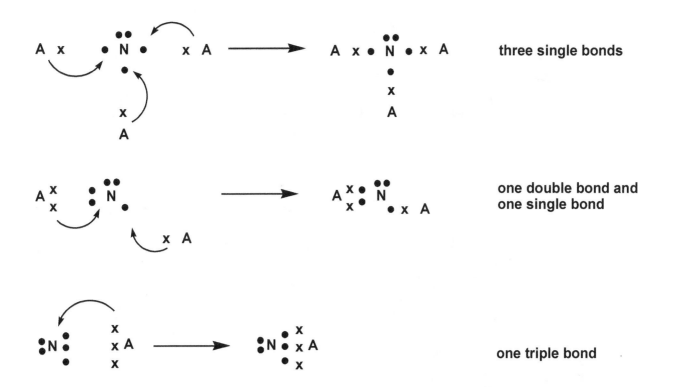

three single bonds

one double bond and
one single bond

one triple bond

Notice that each nitrogen atom has one pair of electrons that is
not a part of a covalent bond. In determining the shape of the
molecule the bonding and lone-pair electrons will be as far
apart from each other as possible just as they were in the
molecules containing carbon.

In summary, the number of valence electrons that an atom has
will determine the number and type of bonds an atom needs to
form to fulfill the octet rule. The arrangement of bonding and
lone-pair electrons determines the shape or geometry of the
molecule which then can be used to make judgments about the
polarity of the molecule.

## Materials Needed

Molecular model kit.

## Safety Precautions

Use normal laboratory precautions.

## Procedure

It is recommended that students work individually for this experiment.

1. Build the following molecules using the molecular model kits: $CH_4$, $NH_3$, $HCl$, $O_2$, $N_2$, $CHBr_3$, $CCl_4$, $CH_2O$, $CO_2$, and $Cl_2$

2. Determine the number and type of bonds that each atom must form in order to fulfill the octet rule. (The pre-drilled holes in the atoms will assist you in this.)

3. Determine whether the molecules are polar or nonpolar based on the electronegativity of the elements and on the molecular geometry.

4. Record your observations

5. **Return the model kit when you have completed the experiment. Clean off your work area and wash your hands thoroughly with detergent and water before you leave the laboratory.**

# CHEMICAL BONDING

Name _____

Date _____

## Prelaboratory Assignment

1. Define octet rule.


2. Define electronegativity.


3. What factors are used to determine whether a bond will be
   polar or nonpolar?


4. What factors are used to determine whether a molecule will
   be polar or nonpolar?

# CHEMICAL BONDING

Name _____

Date _____

## Laboratory Report

**Results**

| Molecular Formula | Drawing of Molecule |
| --- | --- |

$CH_4$

$NH_3$

$HCl$

$O_2$

$N_2$

$CHBr_3$

$CCl_4$

$CH_2O$

$SO_2$

$Cl_2$

## Questions

1. How many SINGLE BONDS do each of these atoms need to fulfill the octet rule?

Carbon: _____

Fluorine: _____

Nitrogen: _____

Oxygen: _____


2. Indicate whether the following molecules are polar or nonpolar based on the bond polarities and the shapes of the molecules.

$CH_4$: _____


$NH_3$: _____


$HCl$: _____


$O_2$: _____


$N_2$: _____


$CHBr_3$: _____


$CCl_4$: _____


$CH_2O$: _____


$SO_2$: _____


$Cl_2$: _____

# CHEMICAL REACTIONS

## Objective

In this experiment, you will visually observe the formation of a new substance as a result of a chemical reaction. You will isolate this new substance and quantitatively determine how much of it is produced in the reaction.

## Introduction

A chemical reaction always involves the conversion of one or more substances, called reactants, into one or more different substances, called products. On the submicroscopic level, a reaction involves the regrouping of atoms or ions to form the new substances. When chemical reactions occur, there are frequently, but not always, changes that can be detected by your physical senses. In the laboratory, you can use your senses of sight, smell, and touch to determine when a chemical reaction occurs. For obvious safety reasons, you are not to use your sense of taste in the lab.

One of the ways you can sense that a chemical reaction has occurred is by observing the formation of a precipitate. A precipitate results when a product of the reaction is insoluble in the solvent being used. This insoluble product may consist of small particles that appear as a cloudy suspension or larger particles that rapidly settle to the bottom of the container. In describing a precipitate, you should always note its color.

A second way of determining that a reaction has occurred is by observing the formation of a gas. Gas evolution involves the formation of bubbles in the reaction mixture when a gaseous product is insoluble in the solvent. Gas evolution occurs in the decomposition of some unstable acids. For example, carbonic acid will form carbon dioxide and water on heating.

$$H_2CO_3(aq) \rightarrow CO_2(g) + H_2O(l)$$

Most gases are colorless and odorless. Some gases have distinctive odors, however, and the sense of smell can be used to identify them.

A third way of determining that a reaction has occurred is by observing a change in the color of the reaction mixture.

Color changes can be quite vivid, especially in oxidation-reduction reactions. In these reactions, one substance loses electrons and is oxidized, while a second substance gains electrons and is reduced.

A fourth way to observe that a chemical reaction has occurred is to detect a change in the temperature of the reaction mixture. When energy is released by the chemicals as a result of a chemical reaction, there is an increase in the temperature of the reaction mixture. Such a reaction is called exothermic. Combustion reactions are exothermic. For example, when methane is burned in a Bunsen burner, heat is produced.

$$CH_4(g) + 2 O_2(g) \rightarrow CO_2(g) + 2 H_2O(g) + heat$$

If energy is absorbed when a reaction occurs, the temperature of the reaction mixture will decrease. Such a reaction is called endothermic. The sense of touch can be used to determine whether a chemical reaction has occurred if sufficient energy is released or absorbed to produce a detectable temperature change. This is done by simply touching the container holding the reaction mixture to determine if it feels warmer or colder.

In general, a chemical reaction is described with a chemical equation. The chemical equation is a statement that represents the reacting species and those produced with formulas and symbols. A proper chemical equation is based on experimental evidence. Simply writing an equation does not mean that the reaction actually takes place. Also, to be in agreement with the Law of Conservation of Mass, the equation must be balanced. Only balanced equations can be used in chemical calculations.

In this experiment, you will observe the reaction that takes place when solutions of calcium chloride and sodium carbonate are mixed. The products are sodium chloride and calcium carbonate. Sodium chloride is soluble in water, and it will remain in solution. Calcium carbonate, however, is insoluble in water, and it will appear as a precipitate. This will be the visible sign that a chemical reaction has occurred. You will collect the calcium carbonate by filtration, dry it, and determine the mass and the number of moles of this product of the reaction.

## Materials

0.2 M sodium carbonate ($Na_2CO_3$) (5 mL per student)
0.2 M calcium chloride ($CaCl_2$) (5 mL per student)

filter paper (1 piece per student)

## Safety Precautions

**Be sure to clean up all spills immediately and to dispose of all waste and excess chemicals in the proper container. Never return excess chemicals to the reagent bottles.**

## Procedure

It is recommended that students work individually for this experiment.

1. **Wear chemical splash-proof goggles at all time while in the laboratory. Your goggles must be approved by your instructor as complying with state eye-protection laws.**

2. Place 5 mL of 0.2 M sodium carbonate solution in a clean 25x200-mm test tube.

3. Carefully add 5 mL of 0.2 M calcium chloride solution to the test tube. Record your observation. Save your reaction mixture by placing the test tube in your test tube rack.

4. Set up a filtration assembly as follows:

   A. Place a clean funnel in a 250-mL Erlenmeyer flask.
   B. Write your initials on the edge of a piece of filter paper, and determine the mass of the filter paper.
   C. Fold the filter paper in half, and then in quarters, producing a cone.
   D. Set the filter paper cone in the funnel with the tip of the cone fitted into the stem of the funnel.
   E. Holding the filter paper in place, wet it using distilled water from your water bottle. Pour out the excess water.

5. Carefully pour the contents of your test tube from step 2 into the funnel. Do not fill the filter paper cone higher than 1/8 inch from the top of the paper.

6. To make sure that all the solid in your reaction mixture is transferred, rinse the test tube two or three times with small portions of distilled water, and transfer the rinse water to the funnel.

7. After all of the liquid has drained into the Erlenmeyer flask, carefully remove the filter paper and its contents from the funnel. Spread out the filter paper on a watch glass.

8. The solid on the filter paper is the calcium carbonate precipitate that was formed in your reaction. Dry the filter paper and this precipitate on the watch glass in the oven.

9. Determine the mass of the dried filter paper with the dried precipitate on it.

10. Calculate the mass and the number of moles of calcium carbonate produced in your reaction.

11. **Once the experiment is completed, clean off all equipment and glassware that you used during this experiment and return them to their proper locations. You must clean off your work area and wash your hands thoroughly with detergent and water before you leave the laboratory.**

# CHEMICAL REACTIONS

Name _____

Date _____

## Prelaboratory Assignment

1. How is a chemical change distinguished from a physical change?

2. List four kinds of observations that can lead you to conclude that a chemical reaction has occurred.

3. How small of a change in temperature do you think you can detect by your sense of touch? How could smaller changes in temperature be detected?

# CHEMICAL REACTIONS

Name _____

Date _____

## Laboratory Report

## Results

1. Volume of sodium carbonate solution        _____

2. Volume of calcium chloride solution        _____

3. Record your observation on mixing these two solutions.




4. Mass of filter paper        _____

5. Mass of dried filter paper and calcium carbonate        _____

6. Mass of calcium carbonate        _____

7. Calculate the number of moles of calcium carbonate produced
   in your reaction. Show your work.




8. Write a balanced chemical equation for the chemical reaction
   that took place in this experiment.

## Questions

1. Balance the following chemical equations.

    A. __ Mg(s) + __ HCl(aq) → __ MgCl$_2$(aq) + __ H$_2$(g)

    B. __NaHCO$_3$(s) + __HCl(aq) → __NaCl(aq) + __H$_2$O(l) + __CO$_2$(g)

    C. __NaHSO$_3$(s) + __HCl(aq) → __NaCl(aq) + __H$_2$O(l) + __SO$_2$(g)

    D. __ FeS(s) + __ HCl(aq) → __ FeCl$_2$(aq) + __ H$_2$S(g)

    E. __ BaCl$_2$(aq) + __ Na$_2$SO$_4$(aq) → __ NaCl(aq) + __ BaSO$_4$(s)

    F. __ Mg(s) + __ O$_2$(g) → __ MgO(s)

2. For each of the chemical equations in question 1, describe observations that you might make in the laboratory to determine that the chemical reaction actually occurs.

    A.



    B.



    C.



    D.



    E.



    F.

# REACTIVITIES OF METALS

## Objective

Your objective in this experiment is to investigate the chemical reactivities of several common metals. By observing reactions of these metals with various test reagents, you will be able to rank the metals from most reactive to least reactive.

## Introduction

The metallic elements exhibit a wide range of chemical reactivities from highly active metals such as sodium and potassium, which react vigorously with many substances, to metals of low activity such as gold and platinum. In many of their reactions, metals displace less active elements from compounds. For example, aluminum reacts with nitric acid and with silver nitrate according to the following chemical equations, which show aluminum displacing less active hydrogen and silver from their compounds.

$$2 \text{ Al(s)} + 6 \text{ HNO}_3\text{(aq)} \rightarrow 2 \text{ Al(NO}_3)_3\text{(aq)} + 3 \text{ H}_2\text{(g)}$$
$$\text{Al(s)} + 3 \text{ AgNO}_3\text{(aq)} \rightarrow \text{Al(NO}_3)_3\text{(aq)} + 3 \text{ Ag(s)}$$

Metal atoms lose electrons in displacement reactions to form cations. For example, Al atoms form $Al^{3+}$ cations in the above equations. The rate and vigor of each reaction will depend to a large extent on the inherent reactivity of the metal. Other factors such as temperature, concentration, and metal particle size also affect reaction rate.

In this experiment, you will investigate reactions of the metals calcium, copper, iron, lead, magnesium, and zinc with water, hydrochloric acid, and copper(II) nitrate solution. The reactions, if they occur, will be displacement reactions as described above. Production of gas bubbles, a color change, precipitate formation, formation of a metallic coating on the reacting metal, and heat generation are observable signs that a chemical reaction is occurring. Only very active metals will react with water, while metals of lower activity will react with hydrochloric acid. Also, any metal that is more active than copper will displace copper from copper(II) nitrate. By observing which reactions occur and which do not, and by observing the relative rates of the reactions, you will be able to determine the order of reactivity of the metals.

## Materials

calcium (1-2 small pieces per group)
copper, iron, lead, magnesium, zinc (6-8 pieces each per group)

6 M hydrochloric acid (5 mL per group)
0.1 M copper(II) nitrate (15 mL per group)
distilled water (18 mL per group)

---

### Safety Precautions

  Do not touch the calcium or lead samples with your bare
hands. Handle the hydrochloric acid carefully. Dispose of
the chemicals (especially the lead) in the proper waste
container.

---

## Procedure

     It is recommended that students work in groups of 2 or 3
for this experiment.

A. Reactions with water

  1. **Wear chemical splash-proof goggles at all time while in the
     laboratory. Your goggles must be approved by your
     instructor as complying with state eye-protection laws.**

  2. Place approximately equal amounts of calcium, copper, iron,
     lead, magnesium, and zinc into separate, labeled 16x150-mm
     test tubes, one metal sample per test tube. In most cases,
     3 or 4 small pieces of the metal sample will be sufficient.
     Only use 1 or 2 small pieces of calcium.

  3. Add 3 mL of distilled water to each test tube and record
     your initial observations on any signs of reaction.

  4. Allow the test tubes to stand for 5 minutes. Record your
     final observations on signs of reaction.

B. Reactions with hydrochloric acid

  1. **Bring your test tubes to the fume hood** and add 1 mL of 6 M
     hydrochloric acid to each of the test tubes above, except

for the one that contains the calcium sample. Gently shake each test tube.

2. Allow the test tubes to stand for 5 minutes. Record your observations on signs of reaction, paying close attention to gas formation and heat generation. Indicate the relative rate, or vigor, of each reaction.

3. After recording your observations, dispose of all the samples in the proper waste container.

C. Reactions with copper(II) nitrate

1. Place approximately equal amounts of copper, iron, lead, magnesium, and zinc (omit calcium) into separate, labeled 16x150-mm test tubes, one metal sample per test tube. In most cases, 3 or 4 small pieces of the metal sample will be sufficient.

2. Add 3 mL of 0.1 M copper(II) nitrate solution to each test tube.

3. Allow the test tubes to stand for 10 minutes. Record your observations on signs of reaction, paying close attention to color changes in the copper(II) nitrate solutions.

4. Carefully pour the solution out of each test tube being sure that you do not lose the metal sample.

5. Dump the metal samples onto a paper towel so that you can examine them. Record your observations, paying close attention to any metallic coatings that may have formed on the pieces of metal.

6. After recording your observations, scrape the pieces of metal off of the paper towel and into the waste container.

7. **Once the experiment is completed, clean off all equipment and glassware that you used during this experiment and return them to their proper locations. You must clean off your work area and wash your hands thoroughly with detergent and water before you leave the laboratory.**

# REACTIVITIES OF METALS

Name _____

Date _____

## Prelaboratory Assignment

1. How do you use a Periodic Chart to determine whether an element is a metal or a nonmetal?

2. A. List some general physical and chemical properties of metals.

   B. Compare these to the general properties of nonmetals.

3. Give chemical symbols for the metals that you will study in this experiment.

   calcium _____          iron _____          magnesium _____

   copper _____           lead _____          zinc _____

4. Give chemical formulas for the test reagents that you will use in this experiment.

   water          hydrochloric acid          copper(II) nitrate

   _____         _____           _____

# REACTIVITIES OF METALS

Name _____

Date _____

## Laboratory Report

## Results

A. Reactions with water

| Metal | Initial observation | Final observation |
|---|---|---|
| calcium | | |
| copper | | |
| iron | | |
| lead | | |
| magnesium | | |
| zinc | | |

B. Reactions with hydrochloric acid

| Metal | Observation | Relative rate |
|---|---|---|
| copper | | |
| iron | | |
| lead | | |
| magnesium | | |
| zinc | | |

C. Reactions with copper(II) nitrate

| Metal | Observation on solution | Observation on metal |
|---|---|---|
| copper | | |
| iron | | |
| lead | | |
| magnesium | | |
| zinc | | |

## Questions

1. Based on your observations, rank the metals studied in this experiment from most reactive to least reactive.

_____  _____  _____  _____  _____  _____

Most                                                                    Least
reactive                                                               reactive

2. Briefly explain how you used your observations to establish this ranking of the metal reactivities.

3. Write balanced chemical equations for the following reactions.

calcium  +  water

magnesium  +  hydrochloric acid

zinc  +  copper(II) nitrate

# THE MOLE CONCEPT

## Objective

This experiment is designed to help you understand the concept of the mole. You will measure out and compare samples consisting of one mole each of three different substances.

## Introduction

Atoms and molecules have such small masses and sizes that chemists are seldom able to deal with them one at a time. When a chemist measures out even very small quantities of substances, huge numbers of atoms and molecules are present. To effectively deal with this problem of handling very large numbers of very small objects, chemists have defined a unit called the mole.

One mole of any compound has a mass equal to the formula mass of the compound expressed in grams. For instance, the formula mass of $CO_2$ is 44.0 amu (12.0 + 16.0 + 16.0 = 44.0). Therefore, one mole of $CO_2$ is 44.0 grams of $CO_2$. Likewise, the formula mass of $(NH_2)_2CO$ is 60.0 amu, and one mole of $(NH_2)_2CO$ is 60.0 grams of this compound. For an element, one mole has a mass equal to the atomic mass of the element in grams. For the elements C and Fe, the atomic masses are 12.0 amu and 55.8 amu, respectively. Therefore, one mole of C is 12.0 grams of C, and one mole of Fe is 55.8 grams of Fe.

Chemists have determined experimentally that one mole of any compound contains $6.02 \times 10^{23}$ molecules of that compound. In other words, 44.0 grams of $CO_2$ contain $6.02 \times 10^{23}$ $CO_2$ molecules, and 60.0 grams of $(NH_2)_2CO$, likewise, contain $6.02 \times 10^{23}$ $(NH_2)_2CO$ molecules. Similarly, one mole of an element contains $6.02 \times 10^{23}$ atoms of that element. Thus, 12.0 grams of C contain $6.02 \times 10^{23}$ C atoms, while 55.8 grams of Fe contain $6.02 \times 10^{23}$ Fe atoms. We can therefore say, as a secondary definition, that a mole is $6.02 \times 10^{23}$ units of something. As you can see from this secondary definition, there is nothing mysterious about the mole concept. Just as we call 12 of anything a dozen and 20 a score, we call $6.02 \times 10^{23}$ units a mole. The number $6.02 \times 10^{23}$ is called Avogadro's number, after the Italian scientist Amedeo Avogadro (1776-1856).

In conclusion, samples consisting of one mole each of different substances will contain equal numbers of atoms or molecules, but the samples will have different masses because of the different formula masses of the substances. A summary of this information for the four substances that were discussed above is given here.

1 mole $CO_2$          = 6.02 x $10^{23}$ $CO_2$ molecules       = 44.0 g $CO_2$
1 mole $(NH_2)_2CO$ = 6.02 x $10^{23}$ $(NH_2)_2CO$ molecules = 60.0 g $(NH_2)_2CO$
1 mole C          = 6.02 x $10^{23}$ C atoms          = 12.0 g C
1 mole Fe         = 6.02 x $10^{23}$ Fe atoms         = 55.8 g Fe

## Materials

distilled water ($H_2O$)
sodium chloride (NaCl)
aluminum (Al)

## Safety Precautions

Use normal laboratory precautions. Since the chemical samples are used only for observational purposes, the sodium chloride and the aluminum do not need to be disposed of in a waste container. These samples may be returned to their original containers.

## Procedure

It is recommended that students work in groups of 2 or 3 for this experiment.

1. **Wear chemical splash-proof goggles at all time while in the laboratory. Your goggles must be approved by your instructor as complying with state eye-protection laws.**

2. Determine the mass of a 50-mL graduated cylinder. Add one mole of distilled water to the graduated cylinder. What mass of distilled water did you add to the graduated cylinder? Record the volume of the sample. Record the number of molecules in the sample.

3. Determine the mass of a 250-mL beaker. Add one mole of sodium chloride to the beaker. What mass of sodium chloride did you add to the beaker? Record the number of formula units in the sample.

4. Determine the mass of a 250-mL beaker. Add one mole of aluminum to the beaker. What mass of aluminum did you add to the beaker? Record the number of atoms in the sample.

5. Summarize and compare your results from steps 1, 2, and 3 by completing the table in section D of the laboratory report.

6. **Once the experiment is completed clean off all equipment and glassware that you used during this experiment and return them to their proper locations. You must clean off your work area and wash your hands thoroughly with detergent and water before you leave the laboratory.**

# FORMULA OF A HYDRATE

## Objective

Your objective in this lab is to determine experimenta ly the formula of a copper(II) sulfate hydrate unknown. You wil. accomplish this by determining the ratio of the moles of products obtained in the thermal decomposition of the hydrate

## Introduction

Many ionic compounds that have been crystallized from aqueous solution appear to be perfectly dry. Yet when heated, they yield large quantities of water in the form of steam. The ionic crystals usually change in form, and sometimes in color, as the water is driven off, indicating that the water was present as an integral part of the crystal structure. Such compounds are called hydrates. When the water is driven out of the hydrate, the resulting compound is said to be anhydrous (without water).

An example of a hydrate is magnesium sulfate heptahydrate, $MgSO_4 \cdot 7H_2O$, where the centered dot ($\cdot$) is a special notation used to designate water of hydration. This formula indicates that the hydrate contains $H_2O$ and $MgSO_4$ in a 7-to-1 mole ratio. Thermal decomposition of this hydrate is described by the following chemical equation. This balanced equation shows that the

$$MgSO_4 \cdot 7H_2O\,(s) \xrightarrow{\Delta} MgSO_4\,(s) \;+\; 7\ H_2O\,(g)$$

decomposition products, $H_2O$ and $MgSO_4$, are formed in a 7-to-1 mole ratio. Both the hydrate formula and the balanced equation for its decomposition give the same ratio of the moles of $H_2O$ to the moles of $MgSO_4$, namely moles $H_2O$/moles $MgSO_4$ = 7/1 = 7. This correlation is the basis of the procedure used in this lab for determining the formula of the unknown hydrate.

In this experiment, you will analyze a copper(II) sulfate hydrate unknown, $CuSO_4 \cdot nH_2O$, in order to determine its formula by finding the value of n. You will thermally decompose the hydrate by heating a sample of known mass in a crucible. If sufficient heat is added, all of the hydrate will decompose to anhydrous copper(II) sulfate and water as shown in the following equation.

$$CuSO_4 \cdot nH_2O\,(s) \xrightarrow{\Delta} CuSO_4\,(s) \;+\; n\ H_2O\,(g)$$

The anhydrous copper(II) sulfate will remain in the crucible as a solid residue, while the water will be driven away as steam under the high-temperature reaction conditions. According to the Law of Conservation of Mass, the difference between the masses of copper(II) sulfate hydrate and anhydrous copper(II) sulfate will equal the mass of the water lost during the reaction. The masses of anhydrous copper(II) sulfate and water can be converted into moles using the respective molar masses. The ratio of the moles of these products will then establish the value of n in the hydrate formula $CuSO_4 \cdot nH_2O$. That is, moles $H_2O$/moles $CuSO_4$ = n/1 = n.

## Materials

copper(II) sulfate hydrate (4-5 g per student)

## Safety Precautions

**The crucible, iron ring, and Bunsen burner will get very hot during the heating process. Handle these objects carefully in order to avoid burns. Also, do not place a hot crucible on the balance. Allow it to cool before determining its mass.**

## Procedure

It is recommended that students work individually for this experiment.

1. **Wear chemical splash-proof goggles at all time while in the laboratory. Your goggles must be approved by your instructor as complying with state eye-protection laws.**

2. Equip a ring stand with an iron ring and a clay triangle.

3. Place a clean, dry, covered crucible in the clay triangle and heat it with a Bunsen burner for 5 minutes. The burner should be adjusted to give a blue, non-luminous flame. The tip of the inner flame cone is the hottest part of the flame and should just touch the bottom of the crucible.

4. Remove the hot crucible from the clay triangle using tongs and allow it to cool on a wire screen. Determine the mass of the covered crucible to the nearest 0.01 g.

5. Place enough copper(II) sulfate hydrate in the crucible to fill it approximately 1/3 to 1/2 full. Observe the physical appearance of the hydrate sample (color, size and shape of crystals, etc.). Replace the crucible cover. Determine the mass of the covered crucible and hydrate sample to the nearest 0.01 g.

6. Calculate the mass of the hydrate sample.

7. Place the covered crucible in the clay triangle and heat gently for 5 minutes. The burner should be adjusted so that the tip of the inner flame cone is about 1 inch from the bottom of the crucible.

8. After this initial gently heating, adjust the burner so that the tip of the inner flame cone just touches the bottom of the crucible. Heat strongly for 10 minutes. If the sample starts to smoke, reduce the heat.

9. Remove the hot crucible from the clay triangle and allow it to cool on the wire screen. Be sure to keep the crucible covered during the cooling period. Determine the mass of the covered crucible and anhydrous residue to the nearest 0.01 g.

10. Replace the covered crucible in the clay triangle and heat strongly for another 10 minutes. Allow the crucible to cool and again determine the mass of the covered crucible and anhydrous residue. If this mass and the mass in step 8 differ by 0.02 g or less, proceed to step 10. If the mass difference is greater than 0.02 g, consult your instructor about the necessity of a third heating.

11. Using the result of the final heating, calculate the mass of the anhydrous residue that remains in the crucible. Using the mass of the hydrate sample and the mass of the anhydrous residue, calculate the mass of the water that was in the original hydrate sample.

12. Observe the physical appearance of the anhydrous copper(II) sulfate. Observe what happens when 5 drops of water are added to this anhydrous residue.

13. Dispose of all waste chemicals in the proper waste container.

14. Determine the formula of the hydrate unknown.

15. Once the experiment is completed, clean off all equipment and glassware that you used during this experiment and return them to their proper locations. You must clean off your work area and wash your hands thoroughly with detergent and water before you leave the laboratory.

# EMPIRICAL FORMULA DETERMINATION

## Objective

In this lab, you will determine the simplest formula of a compound - that is, its empirical formula. To do this, you will measure the mass of each element that is present in a sample of the compound that you prepare.

## Introduction

The composition of a chemical compound is independent of its source, provided it has been purified and separated from all other substances. The composition can be determined by chemically breaking the compound into its component elements. These same elements can be recombined in the proper proportions, as dictated by the composition of the compound, to produce the original compound again. These facts are summarized by the Law of Definite Proportions: When elements chemically combine to form a compound, they do so in a definite proportion by mass. The composition of a compound can be used to determine the simplest, or empirical, formula of that compound.

In this experiment, a sample of magnesium chloride will be prepared by reacting a known mass of magnesium with an excess of hydrochloric acid. From the masses of the magnesium used and the magnesium chloride produced, the mass of chlorine in the sample can be determined. The moles of magnesium and moles of chlorine that are present in the sample can then be calculated from the respective masses as shown below.

$$\text{moles of Mg} = \text{mass of Mg} \times \frac{1 \text{ mole Mg}}{24.3 \text{ g Mg}}$$

$$\text{moles of Cl} = \text{mass of Cl} \times \frac{1 \text{ mole Cl}}{35.5 \text{ g Cl}}$$

The ratio of the moles of magnesium to the moles of chlorine can then be calculated and converted to the smallest whole number ratio of moles. This will determine the subscripts of Mg and Cl in the empirical formula of the magnesium chloride.

## Materials

magnesium (Mg) (1 strip per group)

1.0 M hydrochloric acid (HCl(aq)) (50 mL per group)

evaporating dish (1 per group)

---

## Safety Precautions

Hydrochloric acid is corrosive and can cause severe skin burns. If it comes in contact with your skin, immediately wash the affected area with large quantities of water and notify your instructor. Take care when handling hot objects.

---

## Procedure

It is recommended that students work in groups of 2 or 3 for this experiment.

1. **Wear chemical splash-proof goggles at all time while in the laboratory. Your goggles must be approved by your instructor as complying with state eye-protection laws.**

2. Determine the mass of a clean, dry evaporating dish.

3. Determine the mass of a strip of magnesium. Then place the magnesium in the evaporating dish.

4. In the fume hood, slowly add 50 mL of 1.0 M hydrochloric acid to the evaporating dish. Record your observations.

5. Allow the reaction to continue, still in the fume hood, until no more magnesium is visible.

6. Place the evaporating dish on a hot plate in the fume hood. Adjust the hot plate so that the reaction mixture boils gently. Allow the mixture to boil to dryness. The material remaining in the evaporating dish is magnesium chloride. It may not be completely dry, however.

7. Cool the evaporating dish to room temperature. Describe the appearance of the magnesium chloride.

8. Determine the mass of the evaporating dish and the magnesium chloride.

9. In the laboratory, set up a ring stand with an iron ring and wire screen. Place the evaporating dish on the wire screen, and heat it for three minutes using a Bunsen burner. Allow the evaporating dish to cool to room temperature.

10. Re-determine the mass of the evaporating dish and the magnesium chloride. If the mass loss since the previous determination exceeds 0.05 g, the magnesium chloride was not completely dried in step 5. The heating process should be repeated until the mass loss after successive heatings is less than 0.05 g. At this point, the magnesium chloride will be thoroughly dried.

11. Calculate the mass of chlorine in the magnesium chloride.

12. **Once the experiment is completed, clean off all equipment and glassware that you used during this experiment and return them to their proper locations. You must clean off your work area and wash your hands thoroughly with detergent and water before you leave the laboratory.**

## Procedure

It is recommended that students work in groups of 2 or 3 for this experiment.

A. Preparation and collection of oxygen gas

1. **Wear chemical splash-proof goggles at all time while in the laboratory. Your goggles must be approved by your instructor as complying with state eye-protection laws.**

2. Completely fill 3 Beral pipet bulbs with distilled water using your water bottle. These will be used to collect the oxygen gas by displacement of the water. Store the filled bulbs with the openings pointing upward in the bulb holder.

3. Mark "$O_2$" as a label on a 13x100-mm test tube and fill it 3/4 full with 6% hydrogen peroxide. Using the tip of a micro-spatula, add a very small amount of manganese(IV) oxide to the tube. Observe the test tube immediately after addition of the manganese(IV) oxide.

4. Place a gas-delivery stopper in the mouth of the test tube and allow the reaction to proceed for 5 seconds to flush air from the system. This oxygen-generating unit can be held upright in a 100-mL beaker. Pack the extra space in the beaker with a paper towel to secure the test tube.

5. Place the opening of one of the water-filled pipet bulbs over the top of the gas-delivery stopper and begin to collect oxygen gas. Do not squeeze the bulb as this will force water out of it. Be certain to allow all of the water to be displaced by the oxygen. Store the gas-filled bulb with the opening pointing upward in the bulb holder.

B. Test for oxygen gas – the "glowing splint" test

1. Light your Bunsen burner and position it away from the oxygen-generating unit.

2. Ignite a toothpick using the burner. Gently blow out the toothpick's flame so that only a glowing ember remains.

3. Holding the oxygen-filled pipet bulb horizontally, quickly insert the glowing toothpick into the oxygen. Record your observations.

4. Turn off the Bunsen burner.

C. Relative densities of oxygen and air

1. Using the remaining water-filled pipet bulbs, collect 2 more samples of oxygen as described in step 4 of part A.

2. Simultaneously hold one of these oxygen-filled bulbs with the opening pointing upward and one with the opening pointing downward for a period of 5 minutes. Make certain that no water blocks the openings of the bulbs and do not squeeze them.

3. After 5 minutes, test each of the pipet bulbs for the presence of oxygen using a glowing toothpick as described in part B. Record your observations.

D. Reaction of hydrogen and oxygen gases

1. Using a black marker, draw lines on your 3 pipet bulbs dividing each bulb into 6 sections of equal volume. This will allow you to mix different volumes of hydrogen and oxygen gases. Also, number the bulbs 1 through 3.

2. Completely fill the 3 pipet bulbs with distilled water and store them in the bulb holder.

3. Mark "$H_2$" as a label on a second 13x100-mm test tube and fill it 3/4 full with **6.0 M hydrochloric acid under the fume hood**. Using a micro-spatula, add a small amount of granular zinc to the tube. Observe the test tube after addition of the zinc.

4. Place a gas-delivery stopper in the mouth of the test tube and allow the reaction to proceed for 5 seconds to flush

air from the system. This hydrogen-generating unit can be held upright in a 100-mL beaker. Pack the extra space in the beaker with a paper towel to secure the test tube. Do not have any open flames in the vicinity of the hydrogen-generating unit.

5. Examine the oxygen-generating unit that was assembled in part A. If there is no bubbling action in the reaction mixture, the hydrogen peroxide has been completely decomposed and oxygen gas is no longer being produced. If this is the case, dispose of the reaction mixture in the waste container and recharge the unit as described in steps 2 and 3 of part A. If there is sufficient bubbling, do not recharge the unit.

6. Prepare mixtures of hydrogen and oxygen by collecting samples of both gases in each of the water-filled pipet bulbs from step 2. The graduations on the bulbs allow you to collect and mix different volumes of these gases. Allow a small amount of water to remain in each of the bulbs to act as a seal. Store the gas-filled bulbs with the openings pointing downward in the bulb holder.

   a. In bulb 1, collect 1 volume of hydrogen and 5 volumes of oxygen.
   b. In bulb 2, collect 2 volumes of hydrogen and 4 volumes of oxygen.
   c. In bulb 3, collect 4 volumes of hydrogen and 2 volumes of oxygen.

7. Light your Bunsen burner and position it away from the gas-generating units.

8. Test the reactivity of each of the gas mixtures by igniting each mixture in the burner flame. Bring each gas-filled pipet bulb up to the burner, hold the opening of the bulb approximately 2 centimeters from the flame, and quickly squeeze the bulb. Record your observations paying close attention to the sound produced in each case. Rate the "pops" that you hear as loud, moderate, or soft.

9. **Once the experiment is completed, clean off all equipment and glassware that you used during this experiment and return them to their proper locations. You must clean off your work area and wash your hands thoroughly with detergent and water before you leave the laboratory.**

# BOYLE'S LAW

## Objective

In this experiment you will examine the validity of Boyle's law using air and natural gas.

## Introduction

Gases behave differently from the other two states of matter, solids and liquids, so we have different methods for treating and understanding how gases behave under certain conditions. Gases, unlike solids and liquids, have neither fixed volume nor shape. They are molded entirely by the container in which they are held.

Gases are easily compressible because the atoms and molecules of gases have a lot of space between them. By applying external pressure to a gas sample, the atoms or molecules are forced closer together, compressing the gas. Compressed air occupies less volume than non-compressed air. As a result of this property, gases have low density and easy to compress in comparison with liquids and solids.

Three gas laws relate to the temperature, pressure, and volume of an ideal gas at constant mass are: Boyle's law, Charles's law, and Gay-Lussac's law.

**Boyle's law** deals with the quantitative relationship between the pressure and volume of a gas when the temperature and mass of the gas remains unchanged. It is usually stated as: Pressure times Volume equal a constant (PV = K).

**Charles's law** states that the volume of a gas is **directly proportional** to the absolute temperature (K) of a gas sample at constant pressure and constant mass.

**Gay-Lussac's law** states that for a gas at constant volume and constant mass, the absolute temperature (K) of a gas will increase as the pressure of the gas increases.

In this experiment you will examine the validity of Boyle's law. In other words, you will be testing that the pressure exerted by a gas is inversely proportional to the volume it occupies at constant temperature and constant mass. The pressure of a gas sample changes when its volume changes. Boyle's law can be expressed mathematically as follows:

$$P_1V_1 = \text{constant (at constant temperature and mass)}$$

Where: $P_1$ = initial pressure; $V_1$ = initial volume;

For example, suppose the initial pressure of hydrogen gas is 1.5 atmospheres and its volume is 2.0 liters. Then, based on the above formula its product is:

$P_1V_1 = 1.5$ atm x 2.0 L = 3.0 atm.L

Assume that the volume of the hydrogen gas is increased to 2.5 liters (designated as $V_2$) and the new pressure becomes $P_2$. Since, Boyle's Law states that the corresponding pressure and volume values is a constant at constant temperature and mass, en the new pressure ($P_2$) must be:

$$P_1V_1 = \text{constant} = P_2V_2$$

$$\text{atm} \quad x \quad 2.0 \text{ L} \quad = 3.0 \text{ atm.L} \quad = \quad P_2 \quad x \quad 2.5 \text{ L}$$

$$P_2 = \frac{3.0 \text{ atm.L}}{2.5 \text{ L}} = 1.2 \text{ atm}$$

As long     e temperature and mass of the hydrogen gas does not chan        constant remains unchanged even though the pressure or vol         e sample changes.

A good example o        's Law is the breathing process. When a person breathes out,    e ribs move inward and the diaphragm moves up. Since le   room is available, the molecules in the lungs pack closer toget   r because the volume inside the lungs decrease and the pressure   ncrease.

## Materials

Boyle's Law apparatus
Rubber tube
Stopcock grease
Thermometer

### Safety Precautions

Use organic solvent such as alcohol or acetone to clean the lubricated syringe barrel and plunger. Clean your hands with a towel when you lubricate the syringe barrel with stopcock grease.

## Procedure

It is recommended that students work in groups of 2 for this experiment.

1. **Wear chemical splash-proof goggles at all time while in the laboratory. Your goggles must be approved by your instructor as complying with state eye-protection laws.**

2. Lubricate the plunger and inner surface of the syringe barrel of the Boyle's Law apparatus with stopcock grease.

3. Disconnect the syringe from the gauge and pull the plunger to allow air to get into the syringe. Connect the syringe to the pressure gauge. Do not disconnect the syringe from the pressure gauge until you complete the experiment.

4. Hold your thumb tightly over the end of the tubing fitting to seal it and use your other hand to push the plunger in enough to decrease the volume to about 10 cc. This illustrates the ability of a gas to be compressed.

5. Move the plunger to the following settings: 35.0 cc, 30.0 cc, 25.0 cc, 20.0 cc, 15.0 cc and 10.0 cc. Record the pressure on the gauge of each volume setting on your data sheet.

6. Disconnect the syringe from the gauge and pull out the plunger from the syringe. Attach the rubber tube to the natural gas jet and fill the syringe with natural gas.

7. When the syringe is full with the natural gas turn off the natural gas jet. Immediately, insert the plunger into the syringe and connect the syringe to the pressure gauge.

8. Repeat step 4 and 5 for the natural gas sample.

9. **Once the experiment is completed, clean off all equipment and glassware that you used during this experiment and return them to their proper locations. You must clean off your work area and wash your hands thoroughly with detergent and water before you leave the laboratory.**

# BOYLE'S LAW

Name _____

Date _____

## Prelaboratory Assignment

1. Why does a gas fill its container?

2. What does Boyle's Law tell us about the effect of pressure on the volume of a gas at constant temperature and fixed amount of gas?

3. For a fixed amount of gas at constant temperature, predict the pressure and the volume of the gas as shown in the following table (Hint increase or decrease).

| Initial pressure | Initial volume | Final volume | Final pressure |
|---|---|---|---|
| 700 torr | 150 mL | 1 L | ? |
| 4 atm | 6 L | ? | 6 atm |
| 600 torr | 250 mL | 250 mL | ? |

# BOYLE'S LAW

Name _____

Date _____

## Laboratory Report

## Results

A. Air

| Volume of air (cc) | Pressure of air (lb/in$^2$) | P   x   V |
| --- | --- | --- |
| 35 | | |
| 30 | | |
| 25 | | |
| 20 | | |
| 15 | | |
| 10 | | |

B. Natural gas

| Volume of natural gas (cc) | Pressure of natural gas (lb/in$^2$) | P   x   V |
| --- | --- | --- |
| 35 | | |
| 30 | | |
| 25 | | |
| 20 | | |
| 15 | | |
| 10 | | |

## Questions

1. Compare the individual data of the pressure volume products of experiment A. Do they validate Boyle's Law? Give your comments.

2. Compare the individual data of the pressure volume products of experiment B. Do they validate Boyle's Law? Give your comments.

3. A sample of nitrogen gas, occupies a volume of 400 mL at 2 atm pressure. What pressure must be applied to compress the gas to a volume of 200 mL at constant temperature and fixed amount of gas.

# FACTORS AFFECTING SOLUBILITY

## Objective

Your objective in this experiment is to observe some of the factors that affect the solubility of a solute in a solvent. Also, you will observe differences in the boiling point and the freezing point of a solution compared to a pure solvent.

## Introduction

The solubility of a solid in a liquid is the maximum amount of the solid that will dissolve in a given amount of the liquid at a given temperature. Like density and boiling point, solubility is a physical property. A solid will have different solubilities in different liquids. Some solids have very low solubilities in a given solvent and are referred to as being insoluble. Other solids have much higher solubilities and are said to be soluble. For a soluble solid, however, there is always a solubility limit. The same is true for gases dissolved in liquids.

For solutions of liquids in other liquids, the situation may be different. Some liquids are insoluble in other liquids (gasoline in water), while others are soluble to a limit (ethyl ether in water). Some liquids, however, are completely soluble in other liquids, no matter how much of each is present (ethyl alcohol and water). We say that these liquids are miscible in all proportions.

The extent to which a solute dissolves in a solvent and the rate at which it dissolves depend on several factors. Some of these are the nature of the solute and the solvent, the temperature, and agitation (stirring or shaking).

Nature of the solute and the solvent

Here we use the "like dissolves like" rule as a guideline. The more similar two substances are in bonding characteristics, the more likely that one is soluble in the other. This is not an absolute rule, but it does apply in many cases. Consider polar and nonpolar compounds. The rule suggests that polar solutes dissolve in polar solvents and nonpolar solutes dissolve in nonpolar solvents. Consider ionic compounds. You might suspect that they are soluble in highly polar solvents such as water.

## Temperature

For many solids and liquids that dissolve in a liquid, solubility increases with increasing temperature. For gases, solubility in liquids almost always decreases with increasing temperature. This explains why warm carbonated beverages tend to foam more than cold ones when they are opened. When the beverage is opened, the pressure of the carbon dioxide gas above the liquid is lowered and the dissolved carbon dioxide bubbles out of the liquid. This happens to a greater extent and produces more foam at higher temperatures where the gas is less soluble.

## Agitation

When a solute is added to a solvent and stirred, we see the solute particles at first become dispersed and suspended in the solvent. As stirring continues, however, all of the solute dissolves. If more solute is added to this solution and stirring is continued, again all of the solute dissolves. This process cannot be repeated indefinitely; there is a solubility limit. The solubility of sodium chloride in water at 25 °C is 36.2 g per 100 g of water. If more than 36.2 g of sodium chloride is added to 100 g of water at 25 °C, only 36.2 g will dissolve. The excess solid will not dissolve, but will remain suspended in the solution as long as stirring is continued. It will sink to the bottom of the container when stirring is stopped. Agitation affects the rate at which a solute dissolves, but it does not affect the maximum amount of solute that will dissolve in a given amount of solvent.

## Materials

ethyl alcohol ($C_2H_5OH$) (5 mL per group)

iodine ($I_2$) (0.1 g per group)
boric acid ($H_3BO_3$) (0.1 g per group)
sodium chloride (NaCl) (10 g per group)
copper(II) sulfate pentahydrate ($CuSO_4 \cdot 5H_2O$) (6 g per group)

thermometers (1 per group)
thermometer clamps (1 per group)

## Procedure

   It is recommended that students work in groups of 2 or 3
for this experiment.

A. Nature of the solute and the solvent

   1. **Wear chemical splash-proof goggles at all time while in
      the laboratory. Your goggles must be approved by your
      instructor as complying with state eye-protection laws.**

   2. **Bring your 16x150-mm test tube to the fume hood** and place
      5 mL of ethyl alcohol. Place 5 mL of distilled water into
      a second 16x150-mm test tube. Add two small crystals of
      iodine to each test tube. Mix well. Observe each tube and
      record the solubility of iodine in each of the solvents.

   3. Place a small quantity of boric acid (enough to cover the
      tip of your scoop) into a 25x200-mL test tube and an equal
      quantity of sodium chloride into a second test tube. Add
      distilled water in 2-mL portions to each tube. Shake each
      mixture well after each addition of water. Record the
      volume of water required to dissolve each of the samples.

B. Effect of temperature

Using your mortar and pestle, pulverize approximately 6 g of
copper(II) sulfate pentahydrate.

   1. Measure out two samples of 2.5 g each of the pulverized
      copper(II) sulfate pentahydrate on separate pieces of
      weighing paper.

   2. Place 5 mL of distilled water into each of two 16x150-mm
      test tubes.

   3. Heat the contents of one test tube to a gentle boil by
      passing the tube through the flame of a Bunsen burner. Use
      your test tube holder to handle the tube.

4. Immediately add a 2.5 g sample of pulverized copper(II) sulfate pentahydrate to each test tube and stir.

5. Compare the solubility of the copper(II) sulfate pentahydrate in each of the test tubes. Record your observations.

6. **Once the experiment is completed, clean off all equipment and glassware that you used during this experiment and return them to their proper locations. You must clean off your work area and wash your hands thoroughly with detergent and water before you leave the laboratory.**

C. Effect of a solute on boiling point

   1. Measure out two 3.0 g samples of sodium chloride on
      separate pieces of weighing paper.

   2. Pour 100 mL of distilled water into a 250-mL beaker and
      support the beaker over a Bunsen burner using your ring
      stand, iron ring, and wire screen.

   3. Using a thermometer clamp, suspend a thermometer in the
      beaker so that the tip of the thermometer is about 2 cm
      below the surface of the water. The thermometer should not
      touch the side or the bottom of the beaker.

   4. Heat the water to boiling. Record the boiling point of the
      water.

   5. Add one 3.0 g sample of sodium chloride to the water and
      continue heating. Wait for a moment until the sodium
      chloride dissolves and record the boiling point of the
      solution.

   6. Repeat step 5 using the second 3.0 g sample of sodium
      chloride.

D. Effect of a solute on freezing point

   1. Measure out two 1.0 g samples of sodium chloride on
      separate pieces of weighing paper.

   2. Fill a 100-mL beaker with crushed ice and add 20 mL of
      distilled water.

   3. Hold a thermometer in the ice water mixture and read the
      temperature after three minutes, or as soon as the
      thermometer reaches a minimum temperature. Record the
      freezing point of the water.

   4. Add one 1.0 g sample of sodium chloride to the ice water.
      Using a stirring rod (not the thermometer), stir the
      mixture until the sodium chloride dissolves. Hold the
      thermometer in the mixture and record the lowest
      temperature reached. This is the freezing point of the
      solution.

   5. Repeat step 4 using the second 1.0 g sample of sodium
      chloride.

# FACTORS AFFECTING SOLUBILITY

Name _____

Date _____

## Prelaboratory Assignment

1. What is a solution? Are all mixtures solutions? Are all solutions mixtures?

2. Explain the terms solute and solvent.

3. List all the factors that affect solubility.

4. Explain how the choice of a solvent can affect the solubility of a solute.

# FACTORS AFFECTING SOLUBILITY

Name _____

Date _____

## Laboratory Report

## Results

A. Nature of the solute and the solvent

   1. Solubility of iodine in ethyl alcohol: _____

      Solubility of iodine in water: _____

   2. Volume of water needed to dissolve boric acid: _____

      Volume of water needed to dissolve sodium chloride: _____

B. Effect of temperature

   1. Mass of copper(II) sulfate pentahydrate:

      $1^{st}$ sample _____

      $2^{nd}$ sample _____

   2. Observations on dissolving copper(II) sulfate pentahydrate in water:

      Hot water _____

      Cold water _____

C. Effect of a solute on boiling point

   1. Mass of sodium chloride:    $1^{st}$ sample _____

                                    $2^{nd}$ sample _____

   2. Boiling points:   Water             _____

                        Water + $1^{st}$ sample   _____

                        Water + $1^{st}$ + $2^{nd}$ sample _____

D. Effect of a solute on freezing point

    1. Mass of sodium chloride:       1$^{st}$ sample  _____

                                        2$^{nd}$ sample  _____

    2. Freezing points:    Water                       _____

                               Water + 1$^{st}$ sample     _____

                               Water + 1$^{st}$ + 2$^{nd}$ sample  _____

## Questions

1. Discuss the effect of increasing temperature on the dissolution of copper(II) sulfate pentahydrate in water.

2. What effect does a solute have of the boiling point of a solvent? What effect does a solute have on the freezing point of a solvent?

3. If 9.05 g of sodium chloride are soluble in 25.0 mL of water, calculate the amount of sodium chloride that will dissolve in 135 mL of water.

4. Would you expect the solubility of sodium chloride in water to increase or to decrease if the temperature is changed from 25 °C to 80 °C?

# DETERMINING THE MOLARITY AND PERCENT MASS/VOLUME OF SODIUM CHLORIDE SOLUTION

## Objective

In this experiment you will determine the molarity and percent mass/volume of sodium chloride solution.

## Introduction

A mixture is a combination of two or more substances that are not chemically united and do not exist in fixed proportions to each other. A mixture may be homogeneous or heterogeneous.

A homogeneous mixture has the same uniform appearance and composition throughout. A solution is a homogeneous mixture of two or more substances. Thus, a solution is the same throughout, and every sample of it has the same properties. Solutions are made up of a solute and a solvent.

The solute is a component of a solution that is present in lesser quantity than the solvent. The solvent is the solution component present in the largest quantity. In solutions, the solute is present either as individual ions or individual molecules.

Concentration of a solution is expressed in several concentration units. However, the two most commonly used concentration units are molarity and percent mass per volume (% m/v).

Molarity is defined as the number of moles of a solute contained in 1 L of solution.

$$\text{Molarity (M)} = \frac{\text{number of moles of solute}}{\text{1 liter of solution}}$$

Suppose, a solution is made by dissolving 2.0 moles of NaCl in 4.0 liters of solution has a concentration of 0.5 M. The calculation is:

$$M = \frac{2.0 \text{ moles of solute}}{4.0 \text{ Liters of solution}} = 0.5 \text{ M}$$

Percent concentration by mass/volume is a solution concentration that expresses the amount of solute in 100 mL of solution.

$$\% \text{ mass/volume} = \frac{\text{mass of solute in gram}}{\text{volume of solution in milliliter}} \times 100$$

Suppose, the concentration of solution is made by dissolving 5.0 g of sodium chloride in 250 mL of total solution. To find the percent mass-volume:

$$\% \text{ mass/volume} = \frac{5.0 \text{ g solute}}{250 \text{ mL solution}} \times 100 = 2.00 \%$$

In this experiment you will determine the molarity and percent mass/volume of sodium chloride solution. You will collect the mass of sodium chloride in the unknown solution by evaporating the water from the sample. The mole of sodium chloride can be obtained when the recovered mass of sodium chloride is divided by the formula mass of sodium chloride.

## Materials

Unknown concentration of sodium chloride solution
Hot plate
Top-loading balance

## Safety Precautions

The Erlenmeyer flask will get very hot during the heating process. Use tongs when you take off the flask from the hot plate and handle it very carefully. Allow it to cool before determining its mass. Also, do not touch the hot plate when it is hot.

## Procedure

It is recommended that students work in groups of 2 for this experiment.

1. **Wear chemical splash-proof goggles at all time while in the laboratory. Your goggles must be approved by your instructor as complying with state eye-protection laws.**

2. Clean and weigh a 250 mL Erlenmeyer flask and record the mass of the flask on your data sheet.

3. Measure 20.0 mL of unknown concentration of sodium chloride solution using 50 mL graduated cylinder. Pour the solution into the 250 mL Erlenmeyer flask.

4. Heat the solution using a hot plate. To avoid the sample from splatter use a gentle heat. When the water completely evaporates, use tongs to take off the flask from the hot plate and allow it to cool down to room temperature.

5. Weigh the flask and salt residue. Record the results on your data sheet.

6. Finally, using your data obtain the mass of sodium chloride (salt residue).

7. **Once the experiment is completed, clean off all equipment and glassware that you used during this experiment and return them to their proper locations. You must clean off your work area and wash your hands thoroughly with detergent and water before you leave the laboratory.**

# DETERMINING THE MOLARITY AND PERCENT MASS/VOLUME OF SODIUM CHLORIDE SOLUTION

Name_____

Date_____

## Prelaboratory Assignment

1.  What is the molarity of sodium chloride solution prepared by dissolving 10.0 grams in 100.0 mL of solution?

2.  What is the percent mass/volume of sodium chloride solution made by dissolving 5.0 grams of sodium chloride in 40.0 mL of solution?

3.  What is the percent mass/volume and molarity of sodium chloride solution, if 2.0 grams of salt is collected by evaporating from 30.0 mL of sodium chloride solution?

# DETERMINING THE MOLARITY AND PERCENT MASS/VOLUME OF SODIUM CHLORIDE SOLUTION

Name_____

Date_____

## Laboratory Report

### Results

1. Volume of sodium chloride solution
   (unknown concentration)                    _____

2. Gross (mass of Erlenmeyer flask
   and sodium chloride residue)               _____

3. Tare (mass of Erlenmeyer flask)           _____

4. Net (mass of sodium chloride)             _____

## Questions

1. Using the data you obtained experimentally:

    a. Calculate the molarity of sodium chloride solution.

    b. Calculate the percent concentration (% w/v) of sodium chloride

2. If you evaporated 40.0 mL instead of 20.0 mL of sodium chloride solution, how many grams of sodium chloride could you expect to collect?

# ACIDS AND BASES

## Objective

In this experiment, you will investigate the effects that various acids and bases have on different acid-base indicators. You will also make observations on some common reactions that involve acids and bases.

## Introduction

An acid is described as any substance that increases the hydronium ion concentration when dissolved in water. The hydronium ion, $H_3O^{1+}$ or $H^{1+}$(aq), forms when a proton from the acid combines with a water molecule. The following equations describe the behavior of nitric acid and acetic acid, respectively, when added to water.

$$HNO_3(aq) \ + \ H_2O(l) \ \rightarrow \ H_3O^{1+}(aq) \ + \ NO_3^{1-}(aq)$$

$$HC_2H_3O_2(aq) \ + \ H_2O(l) \ \leftrightarrows \ H_3O^{1+}(aq) \ + \ C_2H_3O_2^{1-}(aq)$$

A base is described as any substance that increases the hydroxide ion concentration when dissolved in water. The following equations describe the behavior of the bases sodium hydroxide and carbonate ion, respectively, when added to water.

$$NaOH(s) \ \ (in \ H_2O) \ \rightarrow \ Na^{1+}(aq) \ + \ OH^{1-}(aq)$$

$$CO_3^{2-}(aq) \ + \ H_2O(l) \ \leftrightarrows \ HCO_3^{1-}(aq) \ + \ OH^{1-}(aq)$$

Acids and bases can be classified as being either strong or weak. These terms reflect the extent to which they produce hydronium or hydroxide ions, respectively, in solution. Hydrochloric acid, HCl, and nitric acid, $HNO_3$, are strong acids because they essentially ionize completely when dissolved in water. On the other hand, acetic acid, $HC_2H_3O_2$, and carbonic acid, $H_2CO_3$, are weak acids because only a small fraction of their molecules ionize in aqueous solution. Sodium hydroxide, NaOH, and potassium hydroxide, KOH, are strong bases. In aqueous solution, these compounds dissociate completely into ions. Aqueous ammonia, $NH_3$(aq) or $NH_4OH$, and the carbonate ion, $CO_3^{2-}$, are weak bases. In aqueous solution, these chemicals react with water to produce only small amounts of hydroxide ion.

The pH of a solution is a measure of its hydronium ion concentration. The defining equation for pH is:

$$pH = -\log[H_3O^{1+}]$$

The brackets, [ ], symbolize molar concentration. In a similar manner, the pOH gives a measure of the hydroxide ion concentration of a solution. The defining equation for pOH is:

$$pOH = -\log[OH^{1-}]$$

In any aqueous solution, the product of the hydronium ion concentration and the hydroxide ion concentration equals a constant, called the ion-product constant $K_w$.

$$K_w = [H_3O^{1+}] \times [OH^{1-}] = 1.0 \times 10^{-14} \quad \text{at } 25°C$$

If the $H_3O^{1+}$ concentration of a solution increases, the $OH^{1-}$ concentration must decrease, and vice versa. Because of this relationship between hydronium and hydroxide ion concentrations, the pH and pOH of a solution are also related.

$$pH + pOH = 14$$

If the pH of a solution increases, the pOH must decrease, and vice versa.

The pH scale is graphically represented below.

| $[H_3O^{1+}]$ | $10^{-0}$ | $10^{-1}$ | $10^{-2}$ | $10^{-3}$ | $10^{-4}$ | $10^{-5}$ | $10^{-6}$ | $10^{-7}$ | $10^{-8}$ | $10^{-9}$ | $10^{-10}$ | $10^{-11}$ | $10^{-12}$ | $10^{-13}$ | $10^{-14}$ |
|---|---|---|---|---|---|---|---|---|---|---|---|---|---|---|---|
| pH | 0 | 1 | 2 | 3 | 4 | 5 | 6 | 7 | 8 | 9 | 10 | 11 | 12 | 13 | 14 |

$\uparrow$

← increasingly acidic      neutral      increasingly basic →

pH < 7 acidic      pH = 7 neutral      pH > 7 basic

## Materials

6 M hydrochloric acid (HCl) (6 mL per group)
3 M hydrochloric acid (HCl) (3 mL per group)
6 M nitric acid ($HNO_3$) (1 mL per group)
6 M sulfuric acid ($H_2SO_4$) (1 mL per group)
6 M acetic acid ($HC_2H_3O_2$) (1 mL per group)
vinegar (1 mL per group)

6 M sodium hydroxide (NaOH) (6 mL per group)
6 M aqueous ammonia ($NH_3$(aq) or $NH_4OH$) (1 mL per group)
saturated calcium hydroxide solution ($Ca(OH)_2$) (5 mL per group)

sodium carbonate ($Na_2CO_3$) (1 g per group)
mossy zinc (Zn) (2 small pieces per group)

red and blue litmus paper (2 strips of each per group)
phenolphthalein solution (1 mL per group)
methyl orange solution (1 mL per group)

---

### Safety Precautions

   Take care when handling acids and bases; they can
cause severe burns on contact with your skin. Wash with
soap and water if you spill acids and bases on your skin.
Clean up all chemical spills immediately.

---

## Procedure

   It is recommended that students work in groups of 2 or 3
for this experiment.

A. Preparation and reactions of acid solutions

   1. **Wear chemical splash-proof goggles at all time while in
      the laboratory. Your goggles must be approved by your
      instructor as complying with state eye-protection laws.**

   2. Put 5 mL of distilled water into each of four 16x150-mm
      test tubes. **Bring your four test tubes to the fume hood**
      and add 3 drops of 6 M hydrochloric acid to the first test
      tube. Add 3 drops of 6 M nitric acid to the second tube.
      Add 3 drops of 6 M sulfuric acid to the third tube. Add 3
      drops of 6 M acetic acid to the fourth tube. Place 1 mL of
      vinegar and 4 mL of distilled water into a fifth test

tube. Thoroughly mix the contents of each test tube using your stirring rod. After stirring each sample, rinse the stirring rod with distilled water before stirring the next sample.

3. Using your stirring rod, transfer 1 drop of each acid solution to a piece of red litmus paper. Rinse the stirring rod with distilled water after each transfer. You may use the same piece of litmus paper for several of the samples simply by placing the drops of acid at different locations on the litmus strip. Record the colors that you observe. Repeat this procedure using blue litmus paper.

4. Add 2 drops of phenolphthalein solution to each test tube. Mix well. Examine the test tubes and record the colors that you observe.

5. Add 2 drops of methyl orange solution to each test tube. Mix well. Examine the test tubes and record the colors that you observe. You may now dispose of these samples.

6. **Bring your test tube to the fume hood** and put 5 mL of 6 M hydrochloric acid in to it. Add a small piece of mossy zinc. Observe for 1 minute and record your observations.

7. Measure out 1 g of solid sodium carbonate on a piece of weighing paper. Transfer the sodium carbonate to a test tube. Add 5 drops of 6 M sulfuric acid **under the fume hood**. Record your observations.

B. Preparation and reactions of base solutions

1. Put 5 mL of distilled water into each of two 25x200-mm test tubes. **Bring your test tube to the fume hood** and add 6 drops of 6 M sodium hydroxide to the first test tube. Add 6 drops of 6 M aqueous ammonia to the second tube. Thoroughly mix the contents of each test tube. Place 5 mL of saturated calcium hydroxide solution into a third test tube.

2. Using your stirring rod, transfer 1 drop of each base solution to a piece of red litmus paper. Rinse the stirring rod with distilled water after each transfer. You may use the same piece of litmus paper for several of the samples simply by placing the drops of base at different locations on the litmus strip. Record the colors that you observe. Repeat this procedure using blue litmus paper.

3. **Bring your test tube to the fume hood** and add 2 drops of phenolphthalein solution to each test tube. Mix well. Examine the test tubes and record the colors that you observe.

4. Add 3 M hydrochloric acid drop-by-drop to the test tube containing the sodium hydroxide solution until a color change occurs. Shake the tube after adding each drop of the acid. Record the number of drops of acid required to produce the color change. Repeat this procedure with the aqueous ammonia and the calcium hydroxide solutions. You may now dispose of these samples.

5. **Bring your test tube to the fume hood** and put 5 mL of 6 M sodium hydroxide in a test tube. Add a small piece of mossy zinc. Observe for 1 minute and record your observations. Compare the result seen here to what happened when zinc was added to hydrochloric acid.

6. **Once the experiment is completed, clean off all equipment and glassware that you used during this experiment and return them to their proper locations. You must clean off your work area and wash your hands thoroughly with detergent and water before you leave the laboratory.**

# ACIDS AND BASES

Name _____

Date _____

## Prelaboratory Assignment

1. Give definitions for the following scientific terms.

   A. acid

   B. base

   C. pH

   D. pOH

   E. $K_w$

2. What does pH measure?

3. Complete the following table.

| $[H_3O^{1+}]$ | $[OH^{1-}]$ | pH | Acid, Base, or Neutral |
|---|---|---|---|
| $1 \times 10^{-4}$ M | | | |
| | $1 \times 10^{-5}$ M | | |
| | | 7 | |
| | $1 \times 10^{-13}$ M | | |

4. A solution has a pOH of 8.7.

   A. What is the pH of the solution? _____

   B. Is the solution acidic, basic, or neutral? _____

# ACIDS AND BASES

Name _____

Date _____

## Laboratory Report

## Results

A. Acid solutions

| Acid | Red litmus | Blue litmus | Phenol- phthalein | Methyl orange |
|------|-----------|-------------|-------------------|---------------|
| HCl | | | | |
| $HNO_3$ | | | | |
| $H_2SO_4$ | | | | |
| $HC_2H_3O_2$ | | | | |
| vinegar | | | | |

Zn and HCl _____

$Na_2CO_3$ and $H_2SO_4$ _____

B. Base solutions

| Base | Red litmus | Blue litmus | Phenol- phthalein | Drops of HCl |
|------|-----------|-------------|-------------------|--------------|
| NaOH | | | | |
| $NH_3(aq)$ | | | | |
| $Ca(OH)_2$ | | | | |

Zn and NaOH _____

## Questions

1. Write a balanced chemical equation to describe the neutralization reaction that occurs when hydrochloric acid and calcium hydroxide are mixed.

2. Explain why the color of the phenolphthalein changed from purple to colorless when hydrochloric acid was added to the basic solutions in step 4 of part B of the procedure.

3. Write balanced chemical equations for the following reactions. Name the products in each of the reactions.

   A. zinc and hydrochloric acid

   B. solid sodium carbonate and sulfuric acid

# LABORATORY CHECK-OUT

## Objective

Your objective is to ensure that the lab is left in a clean, orderly condition after completing your final experiment. You will inventory your equipment and clean your work area.

## Introduction

By the time that students complete the final experiment of the course, their work areas undoubtedly will be dirty, and they probably will have missing or broken equipment. It is important, therefore, that students clean their work areas and inventory their equipment in order to leave the laboratory in a clean, orderly condition. This is a courtesy to subsequent users of the lab, and it is also a matter of safety.

## Procedure

1. Check off each item on the **Check-Out List** as you complete the following steps of the procedure.

2. Remove the contents of your locker, placing all the items on the lab bench.

3. Using your towel, wipe out your locker before replacing any equipment.

4. Using the **CHEMISTRY LOCKER INVENTORY** sheet, make an inventory of your equipment. Return each item to your locker as you check it off the list. Be sure to wash and dry any dirty glassware. Replace any broken or missing items with equipment from the lab supply cabinet. Return extra items and any equipment not on the inventory list to the place indicated by your instructor.

5. Using your towel, wipe off your lab bench and clean around your balance. Remove any debris from your sink.

6. Place your dirty towel in the dirty-towel box.

7. After completing all of the above steps, have your instructor inspect your locker and work area. If all is satisfactory, your instructor will initial your **Check-Out List.**

# LABORATORY CHECK-OUT

Name _____

Date _____

## Check-Out List

1. Locker       _____ cleaned

2. Equipment       _____ cleaned

                        _____ broken and missing equipment replaced

                        _____ extra equipment returned

                        _____ inventory completed

3. Work area       _____ lab bench cleaned

                        _____ balance area cleaned

                        _____ sink cleaned

4. Instructor initials       _____

# LECTURE SUPPLEMENT

---

# COURSE OBJECTIVES

# UNIT-1: MATTER AND ENERGY

After completing this unit, students should be able to:

1.  State the definition of matter and describe the classification of matter scheme.

2.  Explain the difference between pure substances, mixtures, elements, and compounds.

3.  Identify given samples of matter as pure substances or mixtures, as elements/compounds or homogeneous/heterogeneous.

4.  Identify the chemical symbols and names for selected elements.

5.  Know the elements that exist in diatomic form ($H_2$, $N_2$, $O_2$, $F_2$, $Cl_2$, $Br_2$, and $I_2$).

6.  Understand the periodic classification of the elements by atomic number into the periods and the groups or families of the periodic table.

7.  Classify elements as metals, nonmetals, or metalloids using the periodic table.

8.  Know the special names for element groups 1A, 2A, 7A, and 8A.

9.  Explain the differences between physical properties and chemical properties of matter and classify given properties as physical or chemical.

10. Describe the differences between physical changes and the chemical changes of matter and classify given changes as physical or chemical.

11. Explain how heat energy is involved in various physical and chemical changes.

# UNIT – 2: MEASUREMENT OF MATTER

After completing this unit, students should be able to:

1.  State metric units and their abbreviations for length, mass, time, area, volume, density, heat, and temperature.

2.  Know the SI base units (names and abbreviations).

3.  Give numerical values for common metric prefixes such as kilo-, centi-, milli-, and micro-.

4.  Performance measurements in the laboratory using a meter stick, graduated cylinder, and balance.

5.  Express numbers using scientific notation and perform calculations with numbers written in scientific notation.

6.  Solve a variety of unit conversion problems (metric-metric, metric-English, etc.) using the conversion factor method.

7.  Solve a variety of temperature conversion problems involving the Celsius, Kelvin, and Fahrenheit scales.

8.  Know the freezing point and boiling point of water on the three temperature scales.

9.  Define density and explain its significance as a physical property used to help identify samples of matter.

10. Perform a variety of density calculations.

11. Know the use of reference books (*Handbook of Chemistry and Physics, Merck Index*, etc.) to obtain data such as densities, solubilities, melting points, and boiling points.

# UNIT-3: ATOMS AND ELECTRONIC STRUCTURE OF ATOMS

After completing this unit, students should be able to:

1.  Explain the basic concept of atoms and subatomic particles.

2.  State the charge and mass of each of the three fundamental subatomic particles that make up atoms.

3.  Define the terms atomic number, mass number, isotope, atomic mass, and ion and write nuclide symbols for various isotopes and ions.

4.  Describe the electronic structure of atoms in terms of orbitals, subshells, and shells.

5.  Write complete ground state electron configurations for atoms.

6.  Determine the valence shell number and the number of valence electrons for an atom from its electron configuration and draw a Lewis dot symbol for the atom.

7.  Explain the periodic system of classification of the elements.

8.  Use the Periodic Chart to determine the atomic number and atomic mass of a given element, to determine whether a given element is a metal or nonmetal, and to determine the group (chemical family) and the period of a given element.

9.  Determine the valence shell number, the number of valence electrons, and the usual ionic charge of an atom from its position in the Periodic Chart.

10. Explain the basic concepts of a wave and describe how a wave is characterized by a wavelength, frequency, and speed.

11. Describe electromagnetic radiation and list several types of electromagnetic radiation indicating relative wavelengths, frequencies, and energies.

# UNIT-4: COMPOUNDS AND CHEMICAL BONDING

After completing this unit, students should be able to:

1.  State the Octet Rule and explain its use as a basis for describing compound formation.

2.  Define the terms ion, cation, and anion.

3.  Describe ionic bonding and list general properties of ionic compounds

4.  Describe covalent bonding and list general properties of covalent compounds

5.  Draw Lewis structures for a variety of molecules and use them to illustrate bonding pairs of electrons, nonbonding pairs (lone pairs) of electrons, single bonds, double bonds, and triple bonds.

6.  Define the term coordinate covalent bond and write a Lewis structure that illustrates this type of bond.

7.  Predict the general properties of ionic and covalent compounds.

8.  Know names and formulas for the polyatomic ions.

9.  Know how to name metal cations, including use of the Stock system for metals that form more than one type of cation.

10. Know the charges of the group 1A, 2A, and 3A cations and the group 5A, 6A, and 7A anions.

11. Predict formulas for ionic compounds using the charges of the constituent ions.

12. Write names from formulas and formulas from names for binary covalent, binary ionic, and ternary ionic compounds.

13. Know the Greek prefixes that are used in n aming molecular compounds.

14. Know how to name the monatomic nonmetal anions.

15. Name ionic compounds given their formulas and write ionic compound formulas given their names.

16. Name binary molecular compounds given their formulas and write binary molecular compound formulas given their names.

17. Explain the concept of electronegativity and describe the trends in electronegativity values that occur within the periods and the groups of the periodic table.

18. Classify bonds as nonpolar covalent, polar covalent, or ionic using electronegativity differences.

19. Classify molecules as polar or nonpolar using electronegativity values.

# UNIT-5: THE MOLE CONCEPT AND BASIC CHEMICAL CALCULATIONS

After completing this unit, students should be able to:

1.   Explain the mole concept.

2.   State the relationships that exist among moles, numbers of atoms, molecules, or formula units, and grams for a given substance.

3.   Solve a variety of mole-Avogadro number problems using the conversion factor method.

4.   Calculate molecular masses for given covalent compounds and formula masses for given ionic compounds.

5.   Know how to convert mole to mass, mass to mole, mole to molecule, molecule to mole and molecule to mass.

# UNIT-6: CHEMICAL REACTIONS

After completing this unit, students should be able to:

1.  Interpret the symbols used in writing chemical equations.

2.  Identify the reactants and products in a chemical reaction.

3.  Balance chemical equations.

4.  Write a balanced chemical equation given a verbal description of a chemical change.

5.  State the relative number of atoms, molecules, and/or formula units represented in a balanced chemical equation.

6.  State the relative numbers of moles of each chemical represented in a balanced chemical equation.

7.  Recognize oxidation-reduction reactions and oxidation numbers.

8.  Explain the terms exothermic (exogonic) reaction and endothermic (endergonic) reaction.

# UNIT-7: STOICHIOMETRY

After completing this unit, students should be able to:

1.   Determine the relative masses of each chemical represented in a balanced chemical equation

2.   Solve a variety of stoichiometry problems (mole-mole, mole-mass, mass-mass) using the conversion factor method.

3.   Predict the limiting reagent, excess reagent and amount of products formed.

4.   Define actual yield and theoretical yield.

# UNIT-8: PHYSICAL STATE AND INTERMOLECULAR FORCES

After completing this unit, students should be able to:

1.  Distinguish between polar and nonpolar covalent bonds by describing the electronegativity differences between the atoms.

2.  Explain the concept of electronegativity.

3.  Explain the concept of the polarizability of an atom or a molecule and describe the relationships between polarizability and electronegatvity.

4.  Distinguish among polar covalent bonds, nonpolar covalent bonds, polar molecules, and nonpolar molecules.

5.  Know how to predict molecular shape and molecular polarity.

6.  Explain the nature of dipole-dipole forces and ion-dipole forces.

7.  Explain what an induced dipole is and distinguish between an induced dipole and a permanent dipole.

8.  Explain the nature of ion-induced dipole interactions and dipole-induced dipole interactions.

9.  Explain the nature of the dispersion forces that act between atoms and between nonpolar molecules.

10. State the relationship between the strength of dispersion forces and the number of electrons present in an atom or molecule and explain why dispersion forces usually increase with molar mass.

11. Explain why dispersion forces exist among species of all types whether they are neutral or bear a net charge and whether they are polar or nonpolar.

12. Explain the nature of hydrogen bonding and indicate the types of molecules that can form hydrogen bonds.

13. Compare the strength of hydrogen bonding forces to the strengths of other types of intermolecular foces.

14. Draw diagrams that illustrate hydrogen bonding between water molecules, between ammonia molecules, and between water and ammonia molecules.

15. State the general physical characteristics of gases.

16. Define pressure and state the SI unit of pressure.

17. Explain how a barometer works and is used to measure atmospheric pressure.

18. Explain how a manometer works and is used to measure gas pressure.

19. State numerical relationships among the pressure units atm, mmHg, and torr and solve pressure conversion factor problems.

20. State Boyle's law in words and as a mathematical equation.

21. State Charles' law in words and as a mathematical equation.

22. State Gay-Lussac's law in words and as a mathematical equation.

23. Discuss the general physical properties of liquids (Vapor pressure, Boiling point and Surface tension).

24. Discuss the general physical properties of solids (crystalline and amorphous solids).

25. Compare and contrast the solid, liquid, and gaseous states of matter with respect to the attractive forces, freedom of motion, shape, density, and compressibility.

# UNIT-9: SOLUTIONS

After completing this unit, students should be able to:

1.  Define the terms solution, solute, and solvent and identify the solute and solvent in a given solution.

2.  List the general properties of solutions.

3.  Define the term solubility and explain how unsaturated, saturated, and supersaturated solutions are prepared.

4.  Describe how the bonding nature of the solute and solvent, temperature, pressure, solute particle size, and agitation affect the dissolving process.

5.  Draw pictorial representations and write chemical equations for the dissolution of glucose and sodium chloride in water.

6.  Explain the use of molarity, mass/volume, mass/mass and volume/volume percent as concentration units and perform a variety of concentration calculations.

7.  Describe how solutions of a given molar concentration and a given mass/mass percent concentration are prepared in the laboratory.

8.  Define the terms electrolyte and nonelectrolyte and explain the difference between a weak and a strong electrolyte.

9.  Explain the concept of colligative properties.

10.  Describe how these colligative properties with in solution: vapor pressure lowering, boiling point elevation, freezing point depression, and osmotic pressure.

11.  Describe the general application of dialysis membranes.

# UNIT-10: ACIDS AND BASES

After completing this unit, students should be able to:

1.  Define reversible and irreversible reactions.

2.  Describe changes in the concentration of reactants and products as the system approaches dynamic equilibrium.

3.  State the Arrhenius and the Brønsted-Lowry definitions of acids and bases.

4.  Write chemical equations that show what occurs when Arrhenius acids and bases are added to water.

5.  Label the Brønsted-Lowry acids and bases in a given chemical equation.

6.  Give names and formulas for common acids (hydrochloric, sulfuric, nitric, phosphoric, carbonic, and acetic acid) and bases (sodium, potassium, magnesium, and calcium hydroxide and ammonia).

7.  Describe the differences between strong and weak acids and between strong and weak bases.

8.  Describe the auto-ionization of water and explain the formation of hydronium ions.

9.  Define pH and explain the relationships between pH and hydrogen ion concentration and between hydrogen ion and hydroxide ion concentrations.

10. State where pH values for strong acids, weak acids, neutral solutions, weak bases, and strong bases are located on the pH scale.

11. Solve a variety of numerical problems involving the calculation of pH values, hydrogen ion concentrations, and hydroxide ion concentrations.

12. Explain the process of acid-base neutralization and write balanced chemical equations for neutralization reactions.

13. Write balanced chemical equations for reactions between metals and acids and between acids and metal carbonates.

14. Explain the term buffer solution.

15. Describe how buffer solution prepares and functions.

# LECTURE SUPPLEMENT

---

# REVIEW SHEETS

# METRIC SYSTEM

## Introduction

The metric system is a measurement system that was established in France in the 1790s. It consists of a set of base units that correspond to various physical quantities to be measured and a group of prefixes that are used with each base unit to form a series of units having different sizes. Each prefix corresponds to a power of 10. Therefore, each metric unit is related in size to other units of the same type by a power of 10, making the metric system a decimal system of measurement.

Use of the metric system gradually spread from France to many other countries and also to the scientific community. The modern version of the metric system is called the International System of Units, or SI. It is the official system of measurement used by most countries in the world and the system of choice of scientists.

## Common metric units

The following table contains a list of several metric units that will be encountered frequently in the study of chemistry. Some metric-English equivalents are given to help you appreciate the sizes of metric units in comparison to other units. It is very important that you are familiar with the units in this list.

| Physical quantity | Metric unit | Abbreviation | Metric-English equivalent |
|---|---|---|---|
| length | meter | m | 1 m = 39.4 in<br>1 m = 1.09 yd |
| mass | gram | g | 1 lb = 454 g<br>1 oz = 28.3 g |
| time | second | s | 1 min = 60 s |
| volume | liter<br>cubic meter | L<br>$m^3$ | 1 L = 1.06 qt<br>1 gal = 3.79 L |
| heat | calorie<br>joule | cal<br>J | |
| temperature | degree Celsius<br>kelvin | $^{\circ}$C<br>K | 0 $^{\circ}$C = 32 $^{\circ}$F<br>100 $^{\circ}$C = 212 $^{\circ}$F |

# Metric prefixes

In the metric system, units of different sizes are obtained by
using various prefixes in conjunction with the base metric
units. For example, consider units for measuring length. The
base unit is the meter (m). By using the prefix kilo- (k), which
means 1000, we obtain the kilometer (km) as a length unit 1000
times larger than the base unit. The numerical values associated
with the prefixes are always powers of 10 ($1000 = 10^3$). Any
prefix can be used in conjunction with any base metric unit. The
following table contains a list of metric prefixes that will be
encountered frequently in the study of chemistry.

| Metric prefix | Abbreviation | Numerical value |
|---------------|--------------|-----------------|
| mega- | M | 1,000,000 or $10^6$ |
| kilo- | k | 1000 or $10^3$ |
| centi- | c | 0.01 or $10^{-2}$ |
| milli- | m | 0.001 or $10^{-3}$ |
| micro- | μ | 0.000001 or $10^{-6}$ |

The following examples illustrate use of the metric prefixes. In
each example, a metric unit involving a prefix is related to the
base unit and also to another unit involving a different prefix.
Note that the units are always related in size by powers of 10.

Length - megameter    1 Mm = 1,000,000 m = 1000 km

Mass - kilogram       1 kg = 1000 g      = 1,000,000 mg

Length - centimeter   1 cm = 0.01 m      = 10 mm

Volume - milliliter   1 mL = 0.001 L     = 0.1 cL

Time - microsecond    1 μs = 0.000001 s  = 0.001 ms

It is often convenient to reverse some of these relationships.
For example, 1 mL = 0.001 L can be expressed as 1 L = 1000 mL.
These are equivalent expressions conveying the same information.
As additional examples, it is easy to see that 1 cm = 0.01 m is
equivalent to 1 m = 100 cm and that 1 μs = 0.000001 s can be
expressed as 1 s = 1,000,000 μs.

# Derived units

Once certain physical quantities and their units are defined, other physical quantities and their associated units can be derived from these defined quantities. As an example, consider units for measuring area. To determine the area of a rectangle, you would actually measure the length and the width of the rectangle and then compute the area by multiplying the length by the width. If the length and width are measured in meters (m), the area will have units of square meters ($m \times m = m^2$). Thus, the area unit, square meter, is derived from the length unit, meter. The following table contains a list of some derived quantities and some units that can be used to measure these quantities.

| Physical quantity | Defining equation | Possible derived units |
|---|---|---|
| area | area of a rectangle = length x width | $m^2$, $km^2$, $cm^2$ |
| volume | volume of a rectangular solid = length x width x height | $m^3$, $mm^3$, $cm^3$ |
| density | density = mass/volume | $g/cm^3$, $kg/m^3$, $g/mL$, $g/L$ |
| speed | speed = distance/time | $m/s$, $km/s$, $cm/s$, $cm/ms$ |

Numerical relationships between derived units can be obtained, or derived, from other known relationships. For example, area and volume unit relationships can be derived from length unit relationships. The following examples illustrate this.

| Length | Area | Volume |
|---|---|---|
| 1 m = 100 cm | $(1\ m)^2 = (100\ cm)^2$ <br> $1\ m^2 = 10000\ cm^2$ <br> $1\ m^2 = 10^4\ cm^2$ | $(1\ m)^3 = (100\ cm)^3$ <br> $1\ m^3 = 1000000\ cm^3$ <br> $1\ m^3 = 10^6\ cm^3$ |
| 1 in = 2.54 cm | $(1\ in)^2 = (2.54\ cm)^2$ <br> $1\ in^2 = 6.45\ cm^2$ | $(1\ in)^3 = (2.54\ cm)^3$ <br> $1\ in^3 = 16.4\ cm^3$ |

It is very helpful to understand the concept of derived units. You do not need to memorize or look up every possible numerical relationship between units. If you know some key relationships, you can usually derive many other relationships. As seen in the examples above, a knowledge of length units allows you to obtain area and volume relationships. Learn lengths and derive areas and volumes when you need them.

## Additional information and relationships

The following table contains some useful information regarding several metric units. Numerical relationships between different units are listed. These can help you to appreciate the size of a particular unit in comparison to other units, and they can be used as conversion factors in unit conversion problems.

| Physical quantity | Information and conversion factors |
|---|---|
| length | 1 m = 39.4 in = 3.28 ft = 1.09 yd<br><br>1 in = 2.54 cm (exact)     1 km = 0.621 mile<br><br>A U.S. dime is about 1 mm, or 0.1 cm, thick.<br><br>Atoms have diameters of about $10^{-8}$ cm. |
| mass | 1 lb = 454 g     1 oz = 28.3 g     1 kg = 2.20 lb<br><br>A U.S. nickel has a mass of about 5 g.<br><br>Atoms have masses in the range $10^{-24}$ to $10^{-22}$ g. |
| volume | 1 L = 1000 mL = 1.06 qt     1 gal = 3.79 L<br><br>1 mL = 1 $cm^3$     1 $m^3$ = 1000 L     1 $in^3$ = 16.4 $cm^3$ |
| density | 1 g/mL = 1 $g/cm^3$ = 1000 g/L = 1 kg/L = 1000 $kg/m^3$<br><br>1 g/mL = 2.09 lb/qt = 8.35 lb/gal = 62.4 $lb/ft^3$<br><br>Density of water at 4 °C = 1.00 g/mL |
| temperature | The degree sign (°) is not used for Kelvin temperatures.<br><br>A 1 °C temperature change equals a 1.8 °F change.<br>A 1 °C temperature change equals a 1 K change.<br><br>Freezing point of water = 32 °F = 0 °C = 273 K<br><br>Boiling point of water = 212 °F = 100 °C = 373 K<br><br>Absolute zero = 0 K = -273 °C = -460 °F |
| heat | A calorie is the amount of heat needed to change the temperature of 1 g of liquid water by 1 °C.<br><br>1 cal = 4.18 J |

# CLASSIFICATION OF MATTER

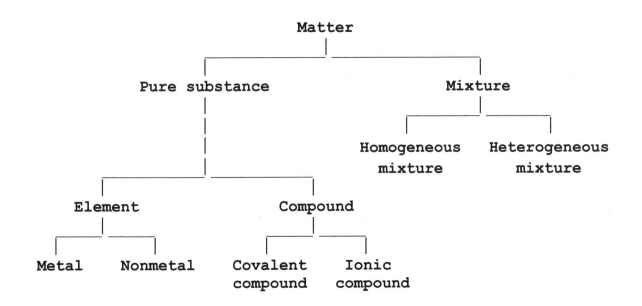

**Matter** – anything that has mass and occupies space

**Mixture** – two or more component substances
  - variable composition
  - component substances retain their chemical identity
  - separate component substances by physical means
  - homogeneous or heterogeneous

**Pure substance** – type of matter that cannot be separated into
  two or more components by physical means
  - fixed, definite composition
  - homogeneous

**Element** – pure substance that cannot be broken down into simpler
  substances by chemical means
  - 114 elements listed on Periodic Chart
  - natural vs. synthetic elements
  - smallest unit is an atom (except diatomic elements)

**Metal** – shiny, metallic luster
  - good electrical conductor
  - good heat conductor
  - solid at room temperature (except mercury)
  - malleable and ductile
  - atom forms cation (positive charge)
  - located to left of stair-step line on Periodic Chart

**Nonmetal** – usually not an electrical conductor
- solid or gas at room temperature (except bromine)
- brittle solid state
- atom forms anion (negative charge)
- located to right of stair-step line on Periodic Chart

**Compound** – pure substance composed of two or more elements
   chemically combined in a fixed proportion by mass
- component elements lose their chemical identity
- separate component elements by chemical means
- millions of compounds

**Covalent compound** – contains two or more nonmetal elements
- solid, liquid, or gas at room temperature
- relatively low melting point (typically below 350 °C)
- typically does not conduct electricity when melted or dissolved in water
- smallest unit is a molecule

**Ionic compound** – contains metal and nonmetal elements
- solid at room temperature
- relatively high melting point (typically above 350 °C)
- conducts electricity when melted or dissolved in water
- smallest unit is a formula unit composed of cations and anions (not a molecule)

# CLASSIFICATION EXAMPLES

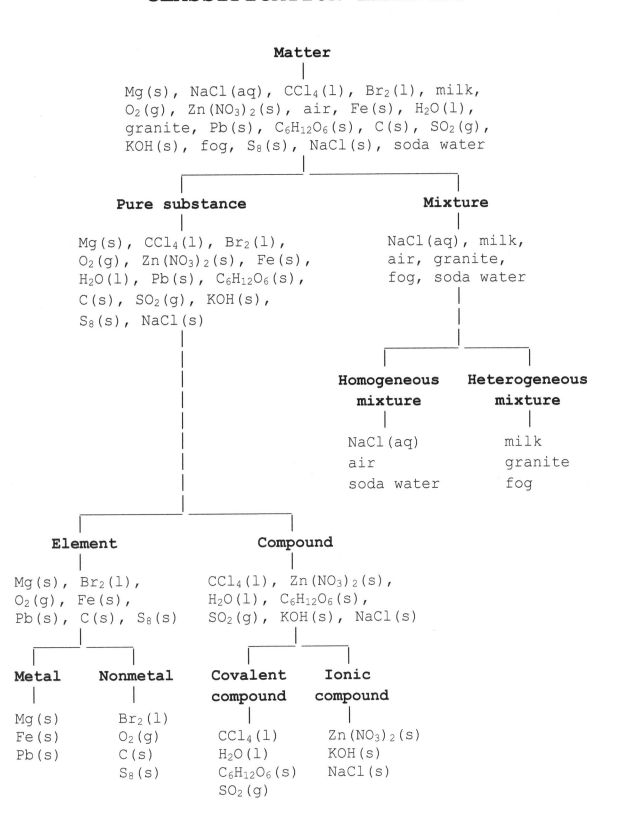

**Matter**

Mg(s), NaCl(aq), CCl$_4$(l), Br$_2$(l), milk,
O$_2$(g), Zn(NO$_3$)$_2$(s), air, Fe(s), H$_2$O(l),
granite, Pb(s), C$_6$H$_{12}$O$_6$(s), C(s), SO$_2$(g),
KOH(s), fog, S$_8$(s), NaCl(s), soda water

**Pure substance**

Mg(s), CCl$_4$(l), Br$_2$(l),
O$_2$(g), Zn(NO$_3$)$_2$(s), Fe(s),
H$_2$O(l), Pb(s), C$_6$H$_{12}$O$_6$(s),
C(s), SO$_2$(g), KOH(s),
S$_8$(s), NaCl(s)

**Mixture**

NaCl(aq), milk,
air, granite,
fog, soda water

**Homogeneous mixture**

NaCl(aq)
air
soda water

**Heterogeneous mixture**

milk
granite
fog

**Element**

Mg(s), Br$_2$(l),
O$_2$(g), Fe(s),
Pb(s), C(s), S$_8$(s)

**Compound**

CCl$_4$(l), Zn(NO$_3$)$_2$(s),
H$_2$O(l), C$_6$H$_{12}$O$_6$(s),
SO$_2$(g), KOH(s), NaCl(s)

**Metal**

Mg(s)
Fe(s)
Pb(s)

**Nonmetal**

Br$_2$(l)
O$_2$(g)
C(s)
S$_8$(s)

**Covalent compound**

CCl$_4$(l)
H$_2$O(l)
C$_6$H$_{12}$O$_6$(s)
SO$_2$(g)

**Ionic compound**

Zn(NO$_3$)$_2$(s)
KOH(s)
NaCl(s)

# ELEMENTS

The following is a list of the elements that will be encountered frequently in the study of chemistry. It is important that you know the names, symbols, and common ions of these elements.

| Element | Symbol | Common ion(s) | Element | Symbol | Common ion(s) |
|---|---|---|---|---|---|
| hydrogen | H | $H^{1+}, H^{1-}$ | calcium | Ca | $Ca^{2+}$ |
| helium | He | | chromium | Cr | $Cr^{3+}$ |
| lithium | Li | $Li^{1+}$ | iron | Fe | $Fe^{2+}, Fe^{3+}$ |
| beryllium | Be | | cobalt | Co | $Co^{2+}$ |
| boron | B | | nickel | Ni | $Ni^{2+}$ |
| carbon | C | | copper | Cu | $Cu^{1+}, Cu^{2+}$ |
| nitrogen | N | $N^{3-}$ | zinc | Zn | $Zn^{2+}$ |
| oxygen | O | $O^{2-}$ | arsenic | As | |
| fluorine | F | $F^{1-}$ | bromine | Br | $Br^{1-}$ |
| neon | Ne | | silver | Ag | $Ag^{1+}$ |
| sodium | Na | $Na^{1+}$ | tin | Sn | $Sn^{2+}$ |
| magnesium | Mg | $Mg^{2+}$ | iodine | I | $I^{1-}$ |
| aluminum | Al | $Al^{3+}$ | barium | Ba | $Ba^{2+}$ |
| silicon | Si | | platinum | Pt | |
| phosphorus | P | $P^{3-}$ | gold | Au | |
| sulfur | S | $S^{2-}$ | mercury | Hg | $Hg_2^{2+}, Hg^{2+}$ |
| chlorine | Cl | $Cl^{1-}$ | lead | Pb | $Pb^{2+}$ |
| argon | Ar | | radon | Rn | |
| potassium | K | $K^{1+}$ | uranium | U | |

Your instructor may add additional elements to this list. Enter them in the following table.

| Element | Symbol | Common ion(s) | Element | Symbol | Common ion(s) |
|---|---|---|---|---|---|
| | | | | | |
| | | | | | |
| | | | | | |

# POLYATOMIC IONS

The following is a list of the polyatomic ions that will be encountered frequently in the study of chemistry. It is important that you know the names, formulas, and charges of these ions.

| Polyatomic ion name | Formula with charge |
|---|---|
| phosphate ion | $PO_4^{3-}$ |
| | |
| carbonate ion | $CO_3^{2-}$ |
| sulfate ion | $SO_4^{2-}$ |
| sulfite ion | $SO_3^{2-}$ |
| | |
| cyanide ion | $CN^{1-}$ |
| hydrogen carbonate ion* | $HCO_3^{1-}$ |
| hydrogen sulfate ion | $HSO_4^{1-}$ |
| hydrogen sulfite ion | $HSO_3^{1-}$ |
| hydroxide ion | $OH^{1-}$ |
| nitrate ion | $NO_3^{1-}$ |
| nitrite ion | $NO_2^{1-}$ |
| | |
| ammonium ion | $NH_4^{1+}$ |

* Commonly called bicarbonate ion.

Your instructor may add additional polyatomic ions to this list. Enter them in the following table.

| Polyatomic ion name | Formula with charge |
|---|---|
| | |
| | |
| | |
| | |
| | |

# ELECTRONIC STRUCTURE OF ATOMS

## Orbitals/quantized energy levels

The electrons in an atom are considered to occupy atomic orbitals. An orbital is a region in space around the nucleus where electrons have a high probability of being found. There are different types of orbitals, with each type having a characteristic electron density distribution, or shape, and a characteristic energy.

The energies of the orbitals are quantized. This means that each orbital in an atom has a fixed, definite energy value that is characteristic of that particular atom. When an electron occupies a certain orbital, it has the energy corresponding to that orbital. Therefore, the orbitals in an atom can also be considered as a set of quantized energy levels that electrons can occupy.

## Electron energy level diagram for atoms

The quantized energy levels, or orbitals, of an atom can be displayed on an energy diagram in order to show their relative energies. In the following diagram, the energy levels are represented by dashes (-).

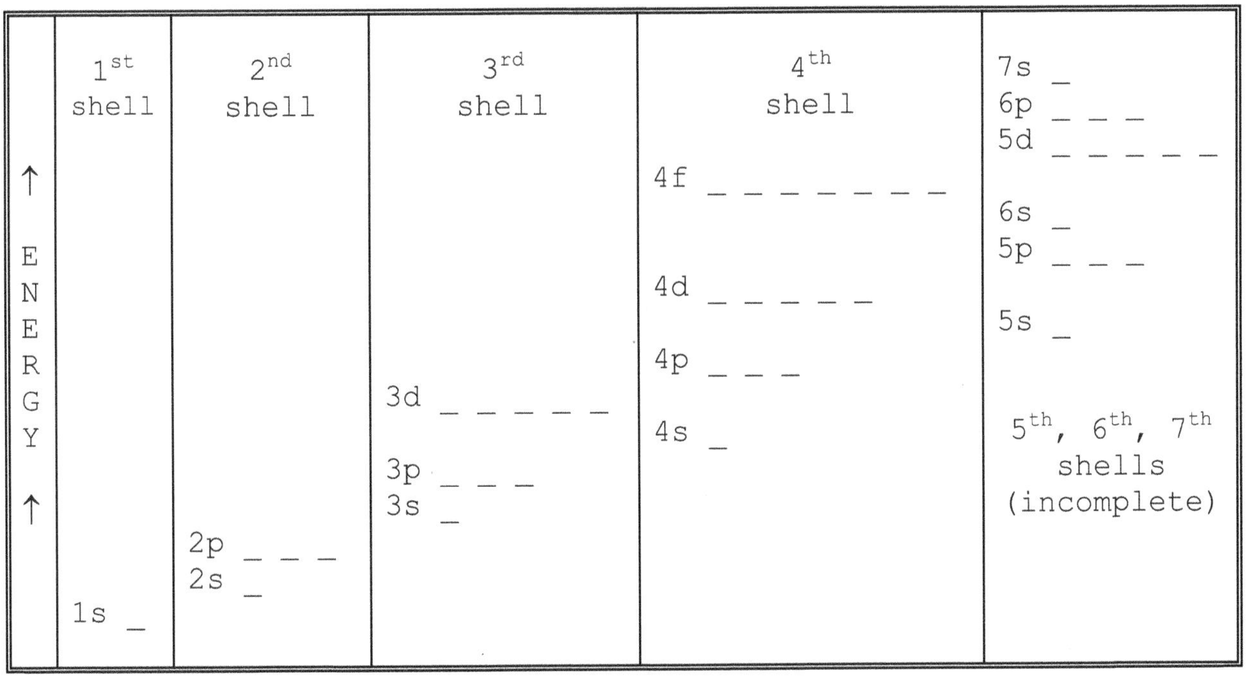

The energy levels can be divided into certain sets based on their energies. Each of these sets of energy levels is called an electron shell, which is identified by an integer number. In general, electrons in higher shells have greater energies and are more likely found farther from the nucleus than electrons in lower shells.

The energy levels, or orbitals, in each shell can be divided into subshells, which are identified by the letters s, p, d, and f. An s subshell contains just one orbital. A p subshell contains three orbitals that are of equal energy. The d and f subshells contain five and seven orbitals, respectively. The number of subshells in a given shell equals the shell number. For example, the $3^{rd}$ shell contains 3 subshells – s, p, and d. By using the shell number and subshell letter, each subshell can be given a unique label (1s, 2s, 2p, etc.).

## Maximum electron capacities

Each orbital, subshell, and shell of an atom has a maximum number of electrons that it can hold. An individual orbital can hold a maximum of two electrons. Using this fact, the maximum electron capacities of the subshells and shells can easily be calculated. This information is given in the following tables.

| Subshell | Number of orbitals | Max. number of electrons |
|----------|--------------------|--------------------------|
| s | 1 | 2 |
| p | 3 | 6 |
| d | 5 | 10 |
| f | 7 | 14 |

| Shell | Subshells present | Max. number of electrons |
|-------|-------------------|--------------------------|
| 1 | s | 2 |
| 2 | s p | 8 |
| 3 | s p d | 18 |
| 4 | s p d f | 32 |

## Order of filling atomic orbitals/energy levels

An atom is normally found in its ground electronic state, which is the lowest energy electronic state of that atom. In order to obtain this lowest energy state, the orbitals of an atom must be filled with electrons in a specific way. We start with the orbital having the lowest energy and place electrons into the orbitals in the order of their increasing energies. An orbital must be completely filled with electrons before we can start filling the next orbital of higher energy. The order in which the orbitals must be filled for the ground electronic state of an atom is obtained by following the arrows in the diagram below. Compare this order with the energy level diagram given above.

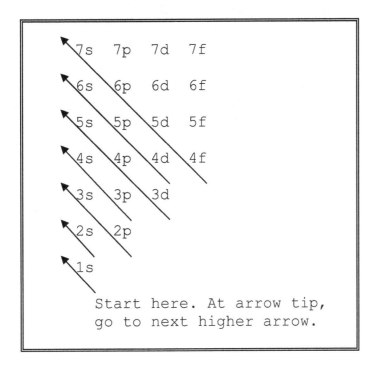

## Electron configurations

The electron configuration of an atom is a statement of how the electrons of the atom are distributed in the various orbitals, or energy levels. We are interested in the ground state electron configuration since an atom is normally found in its lowest energy state. To obtain this electron configurations, we must place the electrons into the orbitals in the order describe above. Also, we must not exceed the maximum electron capacities given above for the orbitals, subshells, and shells.

Ground state electron configurations for several atoms are given below. Each subshell is indicated by its shell number and subshell letter label. The number of electrons in each subshell is indicated by a number written as a superscript.

| | | | |
|---|---|---|---|
| H | $1s^1$ | Na | $1s^2 2s^2 2p^6 3s^1$ |
| He | $1s^2$ | P | $1s^2 2s^2 2p^6 3s^2 3p^3$ |
| | | Ar | $1s^2 2s^2 2p^6 3s^2 3p^6$ |
| Li | $1s^2 2s^1$ | | |
| Be | $1s^2 2s^2$ | K | $1s^2 2s^2 2p^6 3s^2 3p^6 4s^1$ |
| B | $1s^2 2s^2 2p^1$ | Fe | $1s^2 2s^2 2p^6 3s^2 3p^6 4s^2 3d^6$ |
| N | $1s^2 2s^2 2p^3$ | As | $1s^2 2s^2 2p^6 3s^2 3p^6 4s^2 3d^{10} 4p^3$ |
| Ne | $1s^2 2s^2 2p^6$ | Kr | $1s^2 2s^2 2p^6 3s^2 3p^6 4s^2 3d^{10} 4p^6$ |

## Valence shell/valence electrons

The valence shell of an atom is the highest energy shell of that atom. Electrons in this shell are called valence electrons. The valence electrons are more likely found farther from the nucleus than the other electrons in an atom. For this reason, the valence shell is also called the outer shell of an atom. We can obtain information about an atom's valence shell and valence electrons from its electron configuration. Consider the valence information for nitrogen, phosphorus, and arsenic listed in the following table.

| Atom | Electron configuration | Valence shell number | Number of valence electrons | Valence shell configuration |
|---|---|---|---|---|
| N | $1s^2 \underline{2s^2 2p^3}$ | $2^{nd}$ | 5 | $2s^2 2p^3$ |
| P | $1s^2 2s^2 2p^6 \underline{3s^2 3p^3}$ | $3^{rd}$ | 5 | $3s^2 3p^3$ |
| As | $1s^2 2s^2 2p^6 3s^2 3p^6 \underline{4s^2} 3d^{10} \underline{4p^3}$ | $4^{th}$ | 5 | $4s^2 4p^3$ |

Why is it important to know about valence electrons? The answer is that the chemical properties of an element are determined by the number and arrangement of its valence electrons. For example, the chemical properties of nitrogen can be explained by the fact that nitrogen atoms have five valence electrons arranged in the configuration $2s^2 2p^3$.

The vertical columns of elements on the Periodic Table are called chemical families or groups. Elements in the same family have similar chemical properties. The reason for this is that chemical properties are determined by valence electrons, and elements in the same family have the same number and arrangement of valence electrons. Nitrogen, phosphorus, and arsenic are members of the nitrogen family of elements, and, as such, they have some chemical similarities. The table above shows that nitrogen, phosphorus, and arsenic atoms each have five valence electrons arranged in the configuration $ns^2np^3$.

# COMPOUNDS AND CHEMICAL BONDING

## Octet Rule

Elements combine with each other to form compounds. For example, carbon and oxygen combine to form carbon dioxide. In terms of the smallest units that make up substances, atoms of elements bond together to form molecules and formula units of compounds. For example, one carbon atom and two oxygen atoms bond together to form a carbon dioxide molecule.

The basis for understanding chemical bonding in many compounds is the Octet Rule. This rule states that atoms have a tendency to acquire eight valence electrons. This gives them the stable valence shell electron configuration of noble gas atoms.

Atoms can acquire eight valence electrons by sharing pairs of electrons with other atoms or by gaining or losing electrons to form ions. These two different mechanisms that allow atoms to satisfy the Octet Rule lead to two different types of chemical bonding and two general types of compounds. These are covalent and ionic bonding, and covalent and ionic compounds. Covalent compounds are also referred to as molecular compounds.

Atoms that already have eight valence electrons are quite stable and, therefore, do not have a tendency to form chemical bonds. This is the case for the noble gases. With a few exceptions, these elements do not form compounds.

Finally, there are two important exceptions to the Octet Rule. These are hydrogen and helium atoms, which require only two valence electrons.

## Covalent bonding/covalent (or molecular) compounds

1. Nonmetal elements combine with each other to form covalent compounds. Some examples are $CO_2$, $H_2O$, $NI_3$, $C_2H_6$, $SO_3$, $CCl_4$, $C_6H_{12}O_6$, and $H_2SO_4$.

2. When a covalent compound forms from its elements, atoms of the elements share pairs of electrons in order to obtain eight valence electrons and satisfy the Octet Rule. Two nonmetal atoms can share one, two, or three pairs of electrons, and the shared electrons belong to both atoms.

3. In a covalent compound, certain atoms are close enough together to form units in which the atoms share pairs of electrons. Electrical forces of attraction between the shared electrons and each of the two atoms that are sharing them hold the atoms together as a unit. The force of attraction between the atoms and the shared electrons is called a covalent bond. Covalent bonds can be single, double, or triple bonds depending on the number of pairs of electrons that are shared.

4. The smallest unit of a covalent compound is called a molecule. Carbon dioxide is composed of $CO_2$ molecules, each of which consists of one C atom and two O atoms linked together by covalent bonds.

5. A covalent compound is represented by a molecular formula, which gives the exact number of each kind of atom present in a molecule of the substance, and by a Lewis dot formula, which indicates the chemical bonding in a molecule. For carbon dioxide, the molecular formula $CO_2$ and the dot formula :Ö::C::Ö: show that the molecules are composed of one C atom and two O atoms linked together by double covalent bonds.

6. Covalent compounds have certain general properties.

   A. Covalent compounds have relatively low melting points (typically below 350 °C). For example, $H_2O(s)$ (ice) melts at 0 °C.

   B. Covalent compounds are solids, liquids, or gases at room temperature (25 °C), depending on the melting and boiling points of the particular compound. There is not a common physical state for these compounds at room temperature. For example, at 25 °C, $CO_2$ is a gas, $H_2O$ is a liquid, and $C_6H_{12}O_6$ is a solid.

   C. Many covalent compounds, especially organic compounds, are insoluble in water.

   D. Covalent compounds typically do not conduct electricity when melted or when dissolved in water. This results from the fact that these compounds are composed of neutral molecular units. Acids, which conduct electricity because they ionize when dissolved in water, are an exception.

# Ionic bonding/ionic compounds

1. Metal elements combine with nonmetal elements to form ionic compounds. Some examples are NaCl, $K_2S$, MgO, $CaBr_2$, ZnS, $CuCl_2$, $Mg_3N_2$, and NaH.

2. When an ionic compound forms from its elements, atoms of the metal element lose their valence electrons to form positive ions (cations), which have eight electrons in their valence shells and satisfy the Octet Rule. The electrons lost by the metal atoms are gained by the atoms of the nonmetal element to form negative ions (anions), which also obey the Octet Rule.

3. In an ionic compound in the solid state, the cations and anions are packed very close together in a neat, orderly array with cations surrounded by anions and anions surrounded by cations. Electrical forces of attraction between oppositely charged ions hold all the ions together in the solid crystal. The force of attraction between oppositely charged ions is called an ionic bond.

4. The smallest unit of an ionic compound is called a formula unit. Potassium sulfide is composed of $K_2S$ formula units, each of which consists of two $K^{1+}$ ions and one $S^{2-}$ ion linked together by ionic bonds. Since an ionic compound consists of an array of cations and anions, a certain combination of these ions can be selected as a smallest unit of the compound. However, this is not the same as a molecule because these ions are not bonded exclusively to one another as the atoms in a molecule are. A cation in an ionic crystal attracts every anion around it, and vice versa.

5. An ionic compound is represented by an empirical formula, which gives the smallest whole number ratio of the numbers of the different ions present in a sample of the substance. For potassium sulfide, the empirical formula $K_2S$ shows that there are two times as many $K^{1+}$ ions as there are $S^{2-}$ ions in a sample of the compound. This two-to-one ratio of the ions is necessary for the compound to be electrically neutral.

6. Ionic compounds have certain general properties.

   A. Ionic compounds have relatively high melting points (typically above 350 $^\circ$C). For example, NaCl(s) (table salt) melts at 801 $^\circ$C.

B. Ionic compounds are solids at room temperature (25 °C).

C. Many ionic compounds are soluble in water.

D. Ionic compounds conduct electricity when melted or when dissolved in water. This results from the fact that these compounds are composed of positive and negative ions that can readily move when the substance is melted or dissolved.

# SOLUTIONS

## Basic definitions

1. Solution – homogeneous, non-separating (on standing) mixture of two or more substances

2. Solute – substance that is dissolved, usually present in the smaller amount, usually the active component of a solution in chemical reactions

3. Solvent – substance that does the dissolving, usually present in the larger amount, usually the inactive component of a solution in chemical reactions

Consider an aqueous solution of sodium chloride, NaCl(aq). NaCl(s) is the solute, and $H_2O$(l) is the solvent.

In the reaction NaCl(aq) + $AgNO_3$(aq) → $NaNO_3$(aq) + AgCl(s), the NaCl takes an active part in the chemical change, while the $H_2O$ is inactive and does not react.

## Types of solutions

Solutions can be classified according to the physical states of the solute and the solvent. Some examples are given in the following table.

| Solvent → Solute ↓ | Gas | Liquid | Solid |
|---|---|---|---|
| Gas | air (mainly $O_2$(g) in $N_2$(g)) | soda water ($CO_2$(g) in $H_2O$(l)) | $H_2$(g) in Pd(s) |
| Liquid | Do not exist. | ethyl alcohol(l) in $H_2O$(l) | Hg(l) in Ag(s) (an amalgam) |
| Solid | Do not exist. | NaCl(aq) (NaCl(s) in $H_2O$(l)) | brass (Zn(s) in Cu(s)) |

Note that a solution exists in one physical state. For example, when solid NaCl is dissolved in liquid $H_2O$, the resulting solution is liquid.

While several types of solutions are listed in this table, the solutions most frequently encountered in basis chemistry are those that have a liquid solvent.

# Properties of solutions

1. Retention of chemical identity of components

   The physical process of making a solution does not change the chemical identity of either the solute or the solvent.

2. Variable composition

   Aqueous solutions of sodium chloride do not all have the same composition. For example, 5 g of NaCl or 10 g of NaCl can be dissolved in 100 mL of $H_2O$ to form solutions of two different compositions.

   In contrast, chemical compounds have fixed compositions. Every sample of a particular compound contains the same component elements combined in the same definite proportion by mass (Law of Definite Proportions).

3. Separation of components by physical means

   The components of an aqueous solution of sodium chloride can be separated by boiling the solution. At the boiling temperature, sodium chloride is not volatile and will remain behind as the water is converted into steam. The steam can be condensed back into liquid water. Boiling and condensation are physical processes.

4. Homogeneity

   Solutions are always uniform throughout in terms of their composition and properties.

5. Non-separation of components on standing

   For example, compare what happens when sodium chloride, sand, and water are mixed together and stirred. The sodium chloride quickly dissolves in the water. The sand, however, is merely dispersed in the water; it does not dissolve. When stirring is stopped and the mixture is allowed to stand undisturbed, the sodium chloride will stay mixed with the water, while the sand will begin to separate and settle out of the water.

6. Transparency (liquid and gas solutions)

   An aqueous solution of copper(II) nitrate is blue in color, but it is perfectly clear.

# Factors that affect the dissolving process

1. Bonding nature of solute and solvent - "like dissolves like"

   Polar and ionic solutes tend to dissolve in polar solvents.
   Nonpolar solutes tend to dissolve in nonpolar solvents.
   Polar and nonpolar substances tend not to dissolve in one
   another.

   Consider the following common substances.

   | Substance | Bonding nature |
   | --- | --- |
   | water | polar covalent |
   | ethyl alcohol | polar covalent |
   | motor oil | nonpolar covalent |
   | dry cleaning fluid | nonpolar covalent |
   | table salt | ionic |

   Ethyl alcohol and table salt dissolve in water. Motor oil
   dissolves in dry cleaning fluid. Motor oil and water do not
   mix together to form a solution.

2. Temperature - effect on both rate of dissolving and amount of
   solute that dissolves

   Rate: Solids tend to dissolve faster in liquids when the
   temperature is increased.

   Compare the rates at which sugar dissolves in iced tea and in
   hot tea.

   Amount: For most solids, the maximum amount of the solid that
   will dissolve in a given amount of a liquid increases
   when the temperature is increased.

   Compare the maximum amounts of sugar that can be dissolved in
   equal quantities of hot tea and iced tea.

   Amount: For most gases, the maximum amount of the gas that
   will dissolve in a given amount of a liquid decreases
   when the temperature increases.

   Consider what happens when a pan of tap water is warmed on a
   stove. The water contains dissolved air that tends to come
   out of solution and form tiny gas bubbles on the sides of the
   pan as the temperature increases.

3. Pressure - effect on solubility of gases

   Henry's Law: The amount of a gas that dissolves in a given
               amount of a liquid is directly proportional to
               the partial pressure of the gas above the
               liquid.

   Consider the noise that you hear and the bubbles that you see
   when you open a bottle of a carbonated beverage. The noise is
   produced by carbon dioxide gas rapidly escaping from the
   space above the liquid when the bottle is opened. The bubbles
   are produced be dissolved carbon dioxide coming out of the
   liquid in response to the decrease in carbon dioxide pressure
   above the liquid.

4. Solute particle size - effect on rate of dissolving

   Grinding a solid into smaller particles generally increases
   the rate at which it dissolves in a liquid. The grinding
   process increases the surface area of the solid. Increasing
   the surface area over which a liquid can come into contact
   with the solid will increase the rate at which the solid
   dissolves. However, grinding a solid into smaller particles
   will not change the maximum amount of the solid that can be
   dissolved in a given amount of a liquid.

5. Agitation - effect on rate of dissolving

   Stirring or shaking generally increases the rate at which a
   solid dissolves in a liquid. Sugar will dissolve in iced tea
   without stirring, but the process is rather slow. Stirring
   will speed up the dissolution of the sugar. However, stirring
   will not change the maximum amount of sugar that can be
   dissolved in a given amount of the tea.

## Additional terms

1. Solubility - maximum amount of solute that will dissolve in a
               given amount of a solvent at a given temperature

   Consider the solubility of potassium nitrate in water as an
   example. At 25 $^{\circ}$C, a maximum of 38 g $KNO_3$ can be dissolved in
   100 g $H_2O$. At 75 $^{\circ}$C, a maximum of 155 g $KNO_3$ can be dissolved
   in 100 g $H_2O$. A common unit for reporting solubility values is
   grams of solute per 100 grams of solvent.

2. Saturated solution - solution that contains the maximum
amount of solute that will dissolve in
a given amount of a solvent at a given
temperature

The terms "solubility" and "saturated solution" are related.
To measure the solubility of a substance, you must prepare a
saturated solution of that substance.

In addition to being saturated, solutions can be unsaturated
or supersaturated. An unsaturated solution contains less than
the maximum amount of solute that the solvent can dissolve; a
supersaturated solution contains more than the maximum amount
of solute. Supersaturated solutions are usually prepared by
making a saturated solution at a certain temperature and then
cooling the solution to a lower temperature. If precipitation
does not occur, the cooled solution will be supersaturated.

3. Dilution - process of preparing a less concentrated solution
from a more concentrated solution by addition of
solvent

For example, consider that your morning coffee is too strong
for your taste. You add water to the coffee to dilute it and
make it more palatable.

4. Miscible liquids - liquids that mix together to form a
solution

Immiscible liquids - liquids that do not mix together to form
a solution

Water and ethyl alcohol are miscible liquids. Water and motor
oil are immiscible.

5. Electrolyte - substance that conducts electricity when
dissolved in water

Nonelectrolyte - substance that does not conduct electricity
when dissolved in water

Table salt (NaCl, sodium chloride) is an electrolyte, while
table sugar ($C_{12}H_{22}O_{11}$, sucrose) is a nonelectrolyte.

# LECTURE SUPPLEMENT

---

# WORKSHEETS

# SIGNIFICANT FIGURES AND SCIENTIFIC NOTATION

1. Indicate the number of significant figures in each of the following numbers and convert them to or from scientific notation.

   a. 43.55

   b. $5.67 \times 10^2$

   c. 0.00346

   d. $3 \times 10^{-6}$

   e. $2.7 \times 10^3$

   f. 1201.0

   g. 1201

   h. 13004.1

   i. $1.4040 \times 10^6$

   j. $8.0 \times 10^{-2}$

2. Round off each of the following numbers to four significant figures and convert the rounded values to or from scientific notation.

   a. 4,567,985

   b. $2.3581 \times 10^3$

   c. 0.00463537

   d. 90.4483

   e. $9.0373 \times 10^{-5}$

   f. 0.0000083839

   g. $1.938876 \times 10^3$

   h. 200.032

3. Perform the following calculations and express each answer to the correct number of significant figures.

   a. $3.22 \times 0.17$

   b. $4568/1.3$

   c. $22.8 - 0.032$

   d. $0.0003/16$

   e. $(12.3 + 0.092)/8.3$

   f. $328 \times (0.125 + 5.43)$

   g. $21.53 + 0.143 + 3.8$

   h. $1.987/(3.46 \times 10^8)$

4. Perform the following calculations using scientific notation.

   a. $(8.4 \times 10^3) \times (1.6 \times 10^{-5})$

   b. $(4.3 \times 10^3) + (6.8 \times 10^4)$

   c. $(3.2 \times 10^4)/(8.0 \times 10^{-7})$

   d. $(7.3 \times 10^{-5}) - (4.6 \times 10^{-6})$

   e. $(2.8 \times 10^2) \times (4.7 \times 10^{-4})/(1.6 \times 10^{-5})$

# UNIT CONVERSIONS

1. Perform the following metric-metric unit conversions.

   a. $2.85 \times 10^4$ cm to m
   
   b. $7.32 \times 10^2$ g to kg
   
   c. $4.88 \times 10^{-1}$ L to mL
   
   d. $3.65 \times 10^{-2}$ kcal to cal

   e. 1.92 kg to mg
   
   f. 258 mm to cm
   
   g. 0.0657 ms to μs
   
   h. 2750 cm to Mm

2. Perform the following metric-English unit conversions.

   a. 25.3 lb to g
   
   b. 785 cm to in
   
   c. 92700 ms to min

   d. 4.31 qt to mL
   
   e. 0.275 km to mile
   
   f. 3.95 oz to μg

3. Perform the following area and volume conversions.

   a. 0.0263 $km^2$ to $m^2$
   
   b. 4.35 $m^3$ to L
   
   c. 585 $cm^2$ to $in^2$

   d. 1.25 $ft^3$ to $m^3$
   
   e. 75.2 mL to $cm^3$
   
   f. 0.317 gal to mL

4. Perform the following density conversions.

   a. 1.00 g/mL to $g/cm^3$
   
   b. 2.75 $g/cm^3$ to $kg/m^3$

   c. 4.21 $kg/m^3$ to g/L
   
   d. 9.35 lb/gal to g/mL

5. Perform the following temperature conversions.

   a. 98.6 °F to °C
   
   b. 0 K to °F

   c. 212 °F to K
   
   d. −40 °C to °F

# ATOMIC STRUCTURE

1. Characterize the three subatomic particles that make up atoms by completing the following table. (1 amu = $1.67 \times 10^{-24}$ g)

| Particle | Charge | Mass (amu) | Location in atom |
|----------|--------|------------|------------------|
| proton   |        |            |                  |
| neutron  |        |            |                  |
| electron |        |            |                  |

2. Draw a sketch illustrating the Rutherford (nuclear) model of the atom. Indicate how the protons, electrons, and neutrons are arranged in the atom. Give approximate values for the diameter of the nucleus, the diameter of the atom, and the mass of the atom.

3. Complete the following table using the given information and a Periodic Chart.

| Element symbol | Atomic number | Mass number | # of protons | # of electrons | # of neutrons |
|----------------|---------------|-------------|--------------|----------------|---------------|
| Ca             |               | 41          |              |                |               |
|                | 15            |             |              |                | 16            |
|                |               | 65          | 30           |                |               |
| U              |               |             |              |                | 143           |
|                | 17            | 37          |              |                |               |
|                |               |             |              | 56             | 81            |

4. Define the term isotope. Characterize the three isotopes of hydrogen by completing the following table.

| Isotope | # of protons | # of electrons | # of neutrons | Mass (amu) |
|---------|--------------|----------------|---------------|------------|
| $^{1}_{1}H$ |          |                |               |            |
| $^{2}_{1}H$ |          |                |               |            |
| $^{3}_{1}H$ |          |                |               |            |

# ELECTRONIC STRUCTURE OF ATOMS

1. Write a complete electron configuration for each of the following atoms.

   a. H      c. F      e. S      g. Fe

   b. C      d. Mg      f. K      h. Kr

2. Give the valence shell number and the number of valence electrons for each of the following atoms. Also, draw a Lewis electron dot formula for each.

| Atom | Valence shell number | # of valence electrons | Electron dot formula |
|------|---------------------|------------------------|----------------------|
| F    |                     |                        |                      |
| Mg   |                     |                        |                      |
| S    |                     |                        |                      |
| K    |                     |                        |                      |
| Kr   |                     |                        |                      |

3. Indicate whether the following atoms gain or lose electrons to form stable ions. Give the number of electrons that each gains or loses and write a symbol for each ion.

| Atom | Gain or lose electrons | # of electrons | Symbol for ion |
|------|------------------------|----------------|----------------|
| F    |                        |                |                |
| Mg   |                        |                |                |
| S    |                        |                |                |
| K    |                        |                |                |
| Kr   |                        |                |                |

# BONDING AND CHEMICAL FORMULAS

1. State the Octet Rule. Explain two ways in which a sulfur atom can obey the Octet Rule.

2. Predict whether the following substances have ionic, nonpolar covalent, or polar covalent bonds.

   a. $H_2O$        c. $S_8$        e. $SO_2$

   b. $MgCl_2$      d. LiF       f. $H_2$

3. Draw Lewis electron dot formulas for the following molecules.

   a. $H_2O$        c. $CO_2$        e. $SO_2$

   b. $N_2$         d. $CCl_4$       f. HBr

4. Write formulas for compounds containing the following elements.

   a. potassium and chlorine      d. sodium and nitrogen

   b. magnesium and iodine        e. aluminum and sulfur

   c. calcium and oxygen          f. lithium and oxygen

5. Explain how both ionic and covalent bonding are involved in the compound $Ca(NO_3)_2$.

# NOMENCLATURE

1. a. By examining its formula, how can you determine whether a chemical compound is a covalent or an ionic compound?

   b. Why is it necessary to determine this before naming the compound?

2. Name the following binary covalent compounds.

   a. NO          c. $N_2O$        e. $PBr_3$       g. $SF_6$
   b. $NO_2$       d. $N_2O_5$      f. $CS_2$        h. $N_2Cl_4$

3. Name the following ionic compounds.

   a. $Mg_3N_2$         d. $CuCl_2$        g. $Ag_3PO_4$       j. $Ca(HCO_3)_2$
   b. $Mg(NO_2)_2$      e. KBr             h. $Na_2O$          k. $(NH_4)_2S$
   c. $Mg(NO_3)_2$      f. $Ba(OH)_2$      i. $Fe_2(SO_4)_3$   l. $Cu_2CO_3$

4. Write formulas for the following binary covalent compounds.

   a. carbon tetraiodide         e. iodine monobromide
   b. dichlorine trioxide        f. boron trifluoride
   c. arsenic trichloride        g. oxygen difluoride
   d. sulfur dioxide             h. diphosphorus pentoxide

5. Write formulas for the following ionic compounds.

   a. sodium sulfide             g. iron(III) chloride
   b. sodium sulfite             h. zinc sulfide
   c. sodium sulfate             i. copper(II) phosphate
   d. sodium hydrogen sulfate    j. aluminum hydroxide
   e. nickel(II) carbonate       k. lead(II) nitrate
   f. potassium cyanide          l. sodium bicarbonate

# MOLE CALCULATIONS

1. Fill in the blanks. $O_2$ is oxygen gas or elemental oxygen, which exists as a diatomic molecule. O is atomic oxygen, and $O_3$ is ozone.

   1 mole $O_2$ = _____ $O_2$ molecules = _____ g $O_2$

   1 mole O  = _____ O  atoms     = _____ g O

   1 mole $O_3$ = _____ $O_3$ molecules = _____ g $O_3$

2. Calculate the molar mass of each of the following compounds.

   a. NaCl       c. $H_2SO_4$       e. $C_6H_{12}O_6$

   b. $CO_2$       d. $Ca(NO_3)_2$     f. $Fe_2(SO_4)_3$

3. Calculate the number of moles and the number of molecules contained in each of the following samples.

   a. 55 g $CO_2$         c. 1.2 kg $H_2SO_4$

   b. 0.25 g $H_2SO_4$     d. 15 mg $C_6H_{12}O_6$

4. Calculate the mass in grams of each of the following samples.

   a. 0.75 mole $Ca(NO_3)_2$     c. $1.0 \times 10^{25}$ $O_2$ molecules

   b. 1.5 moles NaCl           d. $2.5 \times 10^{20}$ $CO_2$ molecules

5. Calculate the number of oxygen atoms in each of the following samples.

   a. $8.7 \times 10^{21}$ $O_3$ molecules

   b. 15 moles $H_2SO_4$

   c. 100 g $CO_2$

# BALANCING CHEMICAL EQUATIONS

1. Consider the following balanced chemical equation.

$$3 \ Ca(NO_3)_2 \ + \ 2 \ Na_3PO_4 \ \rightarrow \ 6 \ NaNO_3 \ + \ Ca_3(PO_4)_2$$

   a. Identify the reactants and the products in the equation.

   b. What are the numbers in front of each of the chemical formulas called?

   c. How many calcium nitrate formula units are represented on the left side of the equation?

   d. How many calcium phosphate formula units are represented on the right side?

   e. How many oxygen atoms are represented on each side of the equation?

2. Balance the following chemical equations.

   a. __ $CH_4$ + __ $O_2$ → __ $CO_2$ + __ $H_2O$

   b. __ $H_2$ + __ $O_2$ → __ $H_2O$

   c. __ $CaCl_2$ + __ $AgNO_3$ → __ $Ca(NO_3)_2$ + __ $AgCl$

   d. __ $N_2$ + __ $H_2$ → __ $NH_3$

   e. __ $KClO_3$ → __ $KCl$ + __ $O_2$

   f. __ $Al$ + __ $H_2SO_4$ → __ $Al_2(SO_4)_3$ + __ $H_2$

   g. __ $HNO_3$ + __ $Mg(OH)_2$ → __ $Mg(NO_3)_2$ + __ $H_2O$

   h. __ $C_2H_6O$ + __ $O_2$ → __ $CO_2$ + __ $H_2O$

   i. __ $Na$ + __ $H_2O$ → __ $NaOH$ + __ $H_2$

   j. __ $Al$ + __ $O_2$ → __ $Al_2O_3$

# STOICHIOMETRY CALCULATIONS

1. State the relative numbers of moles of the chemicals represented in the following balanced chemical equation. From these values, calculate the relative masses of the chemicals involved in the reaction.

$$H_2SO_4 \ + \ 2 \ NaOH \ \rightarrow \ Na_2SO_4 \ + \ 2 \ H_2O$$

2. State the Law of Conservation of Mass. Show how the relative masses determined in problem 1 can be used to illustrate this law.

3. Perform calculations a-e below using the following balanced chemical equation.

$$C_6H_{12}O_6(aq) \ \rightarrow \ 2 \ CO_2(g) \ + \ 2 \ C_2H_6O(aq)$$

   a. How many moles of $C_6H_{12}O_6$ are needed to produce 15.7 moles of $C_2H_6O$?

   b. How many grams of $CO_2$ are formed by the reaction of $2.58 \times 10^2$ moles of $C_6H_{12}O_6$?

   c. How many grams of $C_2H_6O$ are formed by the reaction of 25.3 grams of $C_6H_{12}O_6$?

   d. How many grams of $C_6H_{12}O_6$ are needed to produce 8.57 millimoles of $CO_2$?

   e. How many grams of $CO_2$ are formed when 2.35 pounds of $C_2H_6O$ are produced?

# ACIDS AND BASES

1. a. State the Arrhenius definitions of an acid and a base.

   b. Write chemical equations that show HCl is an Arrhenius acid and NaOH is an Arrhenius base.

2. a. State the Brønsted-Lowry definitions of an acid and a base.

   b. Identify the Brønsted-Lowry acids and bases in the following chemical equations.

$$H_2S + H_2O \rightleftarrows H_3O^{1+} + HS^{1-}$$

$$NH_3 + H_2O \rightleftarrows NH_4^{1+} + OH^{1-}$$

3. Write chemical equations that show the ionization in aqueous solution of the strong acid HCl and the weak acid HCN. Explain the difference between these equations.

4. Write a balanced chemical equation for each of the following reactions.

   a. __ HCl(aq) + __ NaOH(aq) $\rightarrow$

   b. __ Mg(s) + __ HCl(aq) $\rightarrow$

   c. __ HCl(aq) + __ $Na_2CO_3$(aq) $\rightarrow$

5. Indicate whether the following solutions are acidic, basic, or neutral. A solution with:

   a. pH = 10

   b. $[H^{1+}] = 1 \times 10^{-7}$ M

   c. pH = 2

   d. $[OH^{1-}] = 1 \times 10^{-7}$ M

   e. pH = 7

6. Calculate pH values for the following solutions. A solution with:

   a. $[H^{1+}] = 1 \times 10^{-3}$ M

   b. $[OH^{1-}] = 1 \times 10^{-9}$ M

   c. $[H^{1+}] = 8.53 \times 10^{-9}$ M

   d. $[OH^{1-}] = 4.21 \times 10^{-8}$ M